AFTERSHOCKS AND OPPORTUNITIES 2

Navigating the Next Horizon

www.fastfuture.com

AFTERSHOCKS AND OPPORTUNITIES 2
NAVIGATING THE NEXT HORIZON

First published in United Kingdom by Fast Future Publishing in 2021
www.fastfuture.com

For information contact info@fastfuture.com

Paperback ISBN 978-1-8381955-0-2
eBook ISBN 978-1-9999311-7-9

Cover Designed by Dusan Arsenic

PR and Media Relations by Sam Jones and Paula Hunter, Big Bang PR

Copy Editing and Proof Reading by Steph Bennett, Proof Scrutiny

Interior Design and Typesetting by Consilience Media

Printed in the UK by Print Trail

AFTERSHOCKS AND OPPORTUNITIES 2

Navigating the Next Horizon

Edited by

Rohit Talwar
Steve Wells
Alexandra Whittington

www.fastfuture.com

About Fast Future

Fast Future is a global professional foresight and publishing firm working with leaders in over 70 countries on six continents. We specialize in delivering keynote speeches, executive education, foresight mentoring, research, scenario planning, and consulting to global businesses, investors, governments, and NGOs. Our focus is on identifying the key drivers of change shaping the future landscape, evaluating how they might interact, exploring the scenarios that could play out, and identifying the potential impacts for individuals, communities, society, businesses, and governments.

Fast Future's books provide deep insights on critical factors, trends, developments, advances, and ideas that could shape our collective futures. We draw on contributions from our own team and leading future thinkers from around the world to paint vivid pictures of a rapidly changing operating context. The diverse global insights help our readers to reflect on the potential impact of political and economic forces, socio-demographic shifts, exponential advances in science and technology, and critical environmental developments and challenges.

Fast Future has a particular focus on how we can ensure that the forces, trends, developments, advances, and ideas shaping our world can be harnessed to serve humanity, unleash individual potential, and enable a very human future.

www.fastfuture.com
Twitter @fastfuture
www.facebook.com/FutrBiz
www.linkedin.com/company/fast-future-publishing

The Editors

Rohit Talwar is a global futurist, award-winning keynote speaker, author, and the CEO of Fast Future, working with leaders in global corporations, investment firms, NGOs, and governments. His primary expertise lies in helping clients understand and shape the emerging future. He has a particular focus on how we can advance business, society, and individual lives by harnessing the power of new thinking, innovation, and disruptive developments such as artificial intelligence, blockchain technology, and human enhancement.

Rohit uses cross-disciplinary insights to work with clients to address challenges such as delivering on the Sustainable Development Goals, building system-wide resilience, adapting to the crypto economy, and envisaging the future of business in a "designed for digital" world. He has a deep interest in how we can create a very human future by putting people at the center of the agenda.

Rohit is the co-author of *Designing Your Future*, and lead editor and a contributing author for *The Future of Business*; *Beyond Genuine Stupidity—Ensuring AI Serves Humanity*; *The Future Reinvented—Reimagining Life, Society, and Business*; *A Very Human Future—Enriching Humanity in a Digitized World*; *The Opportunity at the Edge—Change, Challenge, and Transformation on the Path to 2025*; and *Aftershocks and Opportunities—Scenarios for a Post-Pandemic Future*.

rohit@fastfuture.com
Twitter @fastfuture
www.facebook.com/RohitKTalwar
www.linkedin.com/in/rohit-talwar-futurist-keynote-speaker

Steve Wells is a global futurist, keynote speaker, associate consultant with Fast Future, and the CEO of Informing Choices. He has a particular interest in helping clients anticipate and respond to the disruptive bursts of technological possibility that are shaping the emerging future. Steve is a contributor to and co-editor of *The Future of Business; Beyond Genuine Stupidity—Ensuring AI Serves Humanity; The Future Reinvented—Reimagining Life, Society, and Business; A Very Human Future—Enriching Humanity in a Digitized World; Opportunity at the Edge – Change, Challenge, and Transformation on the Path to 2025*, and *Aftershocks and Opportunities - scenarios for a Post-Pandemic Future.*

Web: stevewells.uk
Email steve@stevewells.uk
Twitter @informingchoice
www.facebook.com/stevewells.futurist
www.linkedin.com/in/steve-wells-futurist-speaker

Alexandra Whittington is a futurist with a particular expertise in future visioning and scenario planning. She is a contributor to *The Future of Business*, and a contributor and co-editor for *Beyond Genuine Stupidity—Ensuring AI Serves Humanity; The Future Reinvented—Reimagining Life, Society, and Business; A Very Human Future—Enriching Humanity in a Digitized World; The Opportunity at the Edge—Change, Challenge, and Transformation on the Path to 2025*; and *Aftershocks and Opportunities—Scenarios for a Post-Pandemic Future.*

foresightpartner@gmail.com
Twitter @alexandra4casts
www.linkedin.com/in/alexandra-whittington-futurist

Editorial Assistant

Karolina Dolatowska is a foresight researcher, editorial assistant, and the business manager at Fast Future. She joined the Fast Future team in June 2017. Karolina is a contributor to both *A Very Human Future—Enriching Humanity in a Digitized World*, and *Aftershocks and Opportunities 2: Navigating the Next Horizon*. She has also worked as an editorial assistant on *Beyond Genuine Stupidity—Ensuring AI Serves Humanity; The Future Reinvented—Reimagining Life, Society, and Business; The Opportunity at the Edge—Change, Challenge, and Transformation on the Path to 2025;* and *Aftershocks and Opportunities—Scenarios for a Post-Pandemic Future*.

Karolina@fastfuture.com
www.fastfuture.com
www.linkedin.com/in/karolina-dolatowska-14bab2103

Contents

INTRODUCTION 1

20 Shifts on the Path to 2030, *Rohit Talwar* 17

ECONOMICS AND BUSINESS 33

Life Next: How Our World Could Change Post-Pandemic,
Marian Salzman 34

Blockchain and the Crypto Economy—A Platform for
Transformation? *Rohit Talwar and Kapil Gupta* 38

Envisaging the Accelerated Future of the Crypto Economy,
Kapil Gupta and Rohit Talwar 54

Post-Traumatic Growth: How Might Business Change for the
Better? *Richard Freeman* 66

Business Leadership Skills—Navigating a New Landscape,
Steve Wells 71

Changing the Way We Work, *Steve Wells* 77

The Future of Retirement in the Post-Pandemic Era,
Michael Nuschke 81

THE GLOBAL OPERATING ENVIRONMENT 86

Post-Pandemic Geopolitics: Three Scenarios, *Max Stucki* 87

A World Transformed: Political and Socio-Economic Impacts of
the Pandemic, *Dr. Doaa Alghalban* 91

National Security in the New Normal, *Brett Peppler* 97

Three Possible Futures—Choose Your Preferred Story,
Joana Lenkova 102

The Day After the Lockdown, *Alejandro Repetto* 107

REGIONAL AND NATIONAL FUTURES 112

Reimagining the World Order to Regenerate African,
Caribbean, and Pacific Economies, *Dr. Claire A. Nelson* 113

Futures of a Post-Pandemic Africa, *Leopold P. Mureithi* 117

Greece 2025—If Only We Knew,
Epaminondas Christophilopoulos 122

SOCIETY AND LIFESTYLES 126

Exploring New Normal Futures,
Patrick van der Duin and Hans Stavleu 127

Lockdown Legacy:
How the Pandemic Could Inspire Individual Ownership of
Physical Activity, *Dr. Adam Hawkey* 132

The Digital Health Passport, *Leland A. Shupp* 136

Generational Games: Age Cohort Reactions to the Pandemic,
Arthur Weiss 140

Social Distancing: A Cultural Analysis of the Post-Pandemic
World, *Kevin Jae* 145

Great Reset Day 2025, *Caroline Figuères* 149

Nowhere to Hide in 2025, *Gina Clifford* 153

SECTORAL FUTURES 156

Insurance in the Post-Pandemic World, *David Smith* 157

Collectively Producing Zero-Waste Food:
Zainab's Scenario in 2025, *Dr. Nisreen Lahham* 162

Five Technologies Shaping the Post-Pandemic Future of Food,
Tony Hunter 167

Post-Pandemic Urban Mobility: A Tale of Three Regions,
Boyd Cohen 172

The Reinvention of Travel—and Residency, *Hjörtur Smárason* 178

Post-Pandemic Public Education: Four Scenarios for the United
States, *Jason Siko* 185

Principal's Morning Announcement–Public School 3.16, Brooklyn, New York, September 1st, 2025, *Alisha Bhagat* 190

After the Pause: The Unspoken Futures of Post-Pandemic Higher Education, *Alexandra Whittington* 194

INNOVATION AND TECHNOLOGY 199

Beyond the Pandemic–All Change, *Roger Camrass* 200

Crisis (危機) = Danger (危) + Opportunity (機): A New Renaissance, *José Cordeiro* 205

How the Pandemic Has Become an Accelerant for Virtual Presence, *Cathy Hackl* 209

How Digital Ecosystems Might Shape the Post-Pandemic Recovery, *Greg Wasowski* 213

From Surviving to Thriving the Pandemic: Digital Transformation in Action for Connected Communities, *A. Reza Jafari* 219

A Viridian Aurora, *Frederic Balmont* 224

FUTURE FRAMEWORKS 228

Framework 1: Grand Challenges–Emerging Global Opportunities and Critical Risks, *Rohit Talwar* 229

Framework 2: The Technology Timeline–Advances Shaping the Next Decade, *Rohit Talwar and Karolina Dolatowska* 243

Framework 3: Navigating the Future —50 Critical Questions,
Rohit Talwar and Karolina Dolatowska 259

REFERENCES 266

FAST FUTURE SERVICES AND PUBLICATIONS 269

Fast Future Books and Reports 271

Available soon from Fast Future 279

EXTRACT FROM: AFTERSHOCKS AND OPPORTUNITIES–
SCENARIOS FOR A POST-PANDEMIC FUTURE
– The Change Agenda for a Post-Pandemic World..................280

Introduction

By Rohit Talwar

How can we navigate a sustainable path through the many possibilities, opportunities, and risks that could emerge in our post-pandemic future?

An Incomplete Past and an Uncertain Futures

The world has run out of adjectives to describe the shockwaves caused by the pandemic and the damage it has done to lives, societies, businesses, economies, and entire nations. From overwhelmed health systems, rising unemployment, and chronic mental health problems, through to failed businesses, devasted economies, and a fraying civic infrastructure, the consequences surround us and will leave a lasting legacy. However, in the midst of this continuing global pandemic, we are also witnessing a level of innovation and positive change that most have never experienced in our lifetimes.

Setting aside the rhetoric of building back better, the new normal, and the great reset, what we are seeing is ideas born from necessity, laying down positive foundations to help us transition through and beyond the next horizon. In healthcare, we have seen medical practices transition rapidly to telephone- and video-based appointments, often with higher levels of patient satisfaction and lower risk for medical practitioners. In the pharmaceutical sector, accelerated approaches to vaccine development have been much heralded and are now impacting a broader array of drug development programs.

In education, while some have struggled, many schools, colleges, and universities have made a successful transition to online learning and seen higher levels of student performance as they take on greater responsibility for self-managed learning. Wherever we look, from management consultancy and government services through to restaurants and the retail sector, we see examples of transformations that are likely to last long beyond the point where we could see the virus being managed in a similar manner to flu and the common cold. Perhaps the most—and in some ways least—surprising development has been the accelerated penetration and adoption of information technology applications— ranging from video conferencing to chatbots—to hopefully enhance the employee experience and customer service.

Technological advances have also driven a rise in digital literacy both in the now distributed workplace and in wider society. However, not all technology developments have been positive. Many lost their jobs as a result of automation programs accelerated by the pandemic. Slow moving businesses that failed to adapt to a digital world have seen themselves being overtaken by faster, more digitally centric, and agile competitors. Governments with poor and under-invested technology infrastructures have also struggled to keep pace with the requirements of virtual service delivery.

Navigating the Next Horizon—Enter the Futurists

So where do we go from here? For many, 2019 seems like a period in the far distant past, where a lot of the incomplete challenges, projects, and priorities have been parked or overtaken by a new and rapidly moving agenda born out of a fast-changing present reality and an uncertain future. Navigating this landscape is posing new questions to individuals, organizations, and leaders in every sector. Clearly, no one has the perfect answer for exactly what our different possible futures might look like for individuals, communities, business sectors, nations, and regions across the world. However, futurists and future thinkers have something to offer here.

Futures researchers and practitioners bring a set of tools and perspectives that allow us to consider the driving forces, megatrends, trends, new developments, ideas, possibilities, weak signals of change, wild cards, and black swan events that could shape the future. They use a range of approaches to explore how these future factors may play out and interact with each other, and they allow us to explore the resulting scenarios that could emerge over time.

So, to help us explore the range of possibilities and scenarios that could emerge across the globe over the next decade and beyond, we have brought together 36 futurists and future thinkers from across the globe to share their thoughts on what's next. This truly incredible array of contributions is presented here in *Aftershocks and Opportunities 2— Navigating the Next Horizon*. This book is designed to be a companion volume to the first Aftershocks and Opportunities book published in June 2020. That book also set out to explore the emerging future as seen from the midst of the first wave of the pandemic. The ideas and scenarios presented there are as valid today as they were then.

As with the first Aftershocks and Opportunities book, this latest collection of chapters sets out ideas, insights, provocations, scenarios, and potentially challenging and dystopian possibilities. The book brings together authors from 16 countries ranging from Greenland, Egypt, and Argentina, through to Kenya, the UK, and the US. The regional spread of these contributions encompasses Africa, Asia, Australasia, Central and Latin America, Europe, the Middle East, and North America. We hope you find the book interesting, valuable, and inspiring.

Seven Central Themes

Following the opening chapter exploring some of the critical shifts and disruptions shaping the next five to ten years, the book is divided into seven sections. Our hope is that they will provide insight, perspective, and the motivation to act for citizens, civil society, businesses, and governments across the globe:

Economics and Business—explores the new economic landscape, explains the rise of the crypto economy, discusses the potential for positive change and the value of foresight in business, outlines the leadership skills and organizational capabilities required to navigate a new landscape, and discusses how we can plan for retirement in the post-pandemic era.

The Global Operating Environment—examines scenarios for post-pandemic politics and conflicts, discusses the potential societal implication of this intense period of disruption, explores the paths that individuals, societies, and nations can choose to pursue, and examines the risks and opportunities that lie ahead as we make these choices.

Regional and National Futures—presents bold, fascinating, and truly inspiring perspectives on how to regenerate the regional economies of Africa, the Caribbean, and the Pacific, and highlights how the pandemic-ravaged and struggling Greek economy can reboot itself.

Society and Lifestyles—discusses what "new normal" futures might actually mean, how the pandemic has boosted individual responsibility for our physical wellbeing, and the generational impact of the disruption we've just experienced. The potential benefits and drawbacks of health passports are outlined along with the lasting impacts of social distancing and the downsides of increasing societal surveillance by governments.

Sectoral Futures—looks at the implications of the pandemic and post-disruption recovery strategies for insurance, sustainable agriculture, the broader food sector, urban mobility, travel, and education.

Innovation and Technology—lays out key dimensions of how science and technology can drive the accelerated pursuit opportunities and innovation in a world now more open to fundamental change and transformation. Particular focus is placed on digital architectures and ecosystems, developing digital mindsets, rethinking the innovation agenda, virtual presence, connected communities, and the link between technology and sustainability.

Conclusion: Future Frameworks—the book concludes with three practical frameworks that can act as reference guides and checklists. These explore a diverse range of emerging opportunities and risks and lay out a timeline of critical technologies that could enter the commercial environment in the next one to ten years and beyond. This section also provides a closing set of critical questions for individuals, civil society leaders, businesses, investors, and governments as we seek to plan our individual, societal, and organizational futures.

CONTENTS

To help readers explore the many issues and opportunities on the post-pandemic global change agenda, the scene setting chapter and subsequent seven sections of the book cover the following topics:

20 Shifts on the Path to 2030

Rohit Talwar—Global futurist and CEO, Fast Future, UK

An exploration of twenty emerging developments and weak signals of change that could turn into global forces and societal shifts with a major impact the next decade. These range from the corporatization of home ownership, the rise of an "AI society", and human enhancement, through to zero employee corporations, large-scale job automation, and financial fault lines.

PART 1: ECONOMICS AND BUSINESS

Life Next: How Our World Could Change Post-Pandemic

Marian Salzman—Senior vice president, global communications, Philip Morris International, Switzerland

A look into how life could be forever changed by the pandemic, from a new approach to workplace design to the rise of droids and the emergence of the new 3 Cs: camaraderie, compassion, and community.

Blockchain and the Crypto Economy–A Platform for Transformation?

Rohit Talwar—Global futurist and CEO, Fast Future, UK
Kapil Gupta—Founder of Nibana.life and a technology and crypto analyst, commentator, enthusiast, and investor, UK

Alongside the continual evolution of the pandemic, one of the other big stories of 2021 has been how blockchain technology and the underlying crypto assets it enables, have risen up the agenda for individuals, investors, businesses, and governments. These core concepts are explored and the reasons for the rapid growth in interest are outlined. The risks associated with crypto are discussed, along with the limitations of government issued fiat currencies that crypto assets seek to address, and the impacts of the pandemic on the crypto marketplace. Finally, the potential of the crypto economy to drive a transformation of traditional financial markets is explored.

Envisaging the Accelerated Future of the Crypto Economy

Kapil Gupta—Founder of Nibana.life and a technology and crypto analyst, commentator, enthusiast, and investor, UK
Rohit Talwar—Global futurist and CEO, Fast Future, UK

With the crypto economy now a central focus for businesses and governments alike, an overview is presented of the range of crypto assets and applications that are emerging and the factors driving future adoption. The potential for further market volatility is also discussed and an outline is provided of how the crypto economy might evolve in the coming years.

Post-Traumatic Growth: How Might Business Change for the Better?

Richard Freeman—CEO, always possible

This chapter sets out a hopeful vision for bigger thinking, a rethink of how we talk about "skills," and a call for smarter localized decision-making by businesses in the years ahead.

Business Leadership Skills–Navigating a New Landscape

Steve Wells—Experienced futurist, facilitator, and founder of Informing Choices, UK

This chapter explores three increasingly critical skills to support an evolving leadership model: integrating foresight with change, coaching for complexity and uncertainty in a post-pandemic world, and embedding foresight to help chart our organizations' journeys toward a new landscape. At the heart of navigating a new landscape are invoking human-centric thinking in change and maximizing the effectiveness of the human–technology partnership.

Changing the Way We Work

Steve Wells—Experienced futurist, facilitator, and founder of Informing Choices, UK

Rather than focus on the number of jobs and types of work that we might see in the future, this chapter focuses on how the nature of continuous change could impact work and how the working environment might change. To establish new working norms in the face of continuous change, we will be challenged to consider a new mindset and look at enhancing leadership capability. The way we work is likely to be set by increasing our understanding of the emerging future and re-setting organizational cultural norms.

The Future of Retirement in the Post-Pandemic Era

Michael Nuschke—Retirement futurist, writer, and speaker, Canada/ Mexico

The pandemic will accelerate changes in many areas that impact retirement planning. While the financial implications are negative, these rapid changes may be enough to trigger a new perspective on retirement altogether. The most transformative change will be progress on rejuvenation therapies—an optimal cure for our retirement crisis.

PART 2: THE GLOBAL OPERATING ENVIRONMENT

Post-Pandemic Geopolitics: Three Scenarios
Max Stucki—Foresight analysis manager at Futures Platform, Finland
The pandemic could accelerate the most important geopolitical changes currently in progress. This chapter explores how the geopolitical future of the US, China, and Europe could look after the pandemic.

A World Transformed: Political and Socio-Economic Impacts of the Pandemic
Dr. Doaa Alghalban—Strategic advisor on foresight strategies in the United Arab Emirates (UAE)
The 2020 pandemic has had huge ramifications on the political, social, and economic aspects of the global information economy to the extent that the world will no longer be the same. This chapter answers the question of "what next?" and predicts that there will be an emergence of new influential powers among the Eastern countries which will gain political clout on the basis of their economic and social advantages. Addressing the extent of the damage to society will require enduring partnerships among all nations.

National Security in the New Normal
Brett Peppler—Managing director of Intelligent Futures Pty Ltd, Australia
National security planning is founded on two key concerns: articulation of national interests, and the exercise of national power in pursuit of those interests. These concepts are used to construct four scenarios to illustrate the determinants of national security planning in the new normal over the next two to five years.

Three Possible Futures—Choose Your Preferred Story
Joana Lenkova—Strategist, futurist, and founder of Futures Forward, UK
In times of uncertainty and crisis, our initial instinctive response is to stick to what we know. However, our current volatile reality provides us with the unique opportunity to build a new, better future. Here you will find three possible future scenarios that may become a reality sooner

than we think. Whether they do, and how we realize our preferred future, depends on the decisions taken today.

The Day After the Lockdown

Alejandro Repetto—Foresight and innovation strategy practitioner and co-founder of Robosophy, Argentina

The instability of the present kindles numerous potential futures. Many parts of the world will be forever changed. This chapter describes one of these possible futures, full of risks and opportunities for both governments and companies. The aim is to describe how things may change in workplaces, business, and everyday life, and calls on the decision makers to take action.

PART 3: REGIONAL AND NATIONAL FUTURES

Reimagining the World Order to Regenerate African, Caribbean, and Pacific Economies

Dr. Claire A. Nelson—Lead futurist at The Futures Forum, US

In this scenario, the imperative of regenerative economics underpinning the Ubuntu Economic Agenda has delivered handsome dividends in propelling the African Caribbean Pacific Alliance nations toward 2030.

Futures of a Post-Pandemic Africa

Leopold P. Mureithi—Professor of Economics at the University of Nairobi, Kenya

Even as the world is in the thick of a pandemic, one could wonder: what will the future of a typical African country look like when the crisis is finally over? This chapter explores the developmental choices likely to face a typical African country.

Greece 2025–If Only We Knew

Epaminondas Christophilopoulos—UNESCO chair on Futures Research, and head of the Foresight and Tools Unit in the Hellas Foundation for Research and Technology (FORTH), Greece

In 2020, Greece had just started to recover from a deep economic crisis. In this scenario, five years after that crisis started, Greece is still struggling to adapt to the new reality, while the 3S rule (Sustainability, Self-sufficiency, and Social Accountability) is disrupting everything.

PART 4: SOCIETY AND LIFESTYLES

Exploring New Normal Futures

Patrick van der Duin—Managing director of the Stichting Toekomstbeeld der Techniek, Netherlands
Hans Stavleu—Lead future explorer at curiozy.net., Netherlands

To think about society after the pandemic crisis we have to explore "various" normal futures to anticipate new possibilities and investigate to what extent our old society will, can, or should hold.

Lockdown Legacy: How the Pandemic Could Inspire Individual Ownership of Physical Activity

Dr. Adam Hawkey—Associate professor at Solent University Southampton, UK

The pandemic was accompanied by lockdowns and strict measures of physical distancing. Fast forward to 2025 and the legacy of this lockdown is a positive change in exercise behavior. More empowered to take ownership of their physical activity, society has forged an optimistic future for public health provision.

The Digital Health Passport

Leland Shupp—Foresight and design led company growth strategist and principal at Lee Shupp Consulting, US

The persistence of the pandemic leads to two classes of citizens: "Vaxxed" with antibodies, and the "Anti-Vaxxed" or "Vulnerables" who remain at risk. This leads to the creation of a Digital Health Passport which quickly becomes a useful tool for much more detailed health monitoring.

Generational Games: Age Cohort Reactions to the Pandemic

Arthur Weiss—CEO of AWARE, UK
The way different age groups will respond to the post-pandemic period over the next 2–5 years will not be homogenous, and understanding the differences is important in any future planning.

Social Distancing: A Cultural Analysis of the Post-Pandemic World

Kevin Jae—Research assistant at the Diversity Institute, Canada
The pandemic exposes the vulnerabilities of the contemporary, globalized world. An effective response involves a restructuring of societal structures, which leads to the emergence of a new culture. The chapter explores the contours of this new culture.

Great Reset Day 2025

Caroline Figuères—Director of Figueres Consultancy, Netherlands
This chapter presents a scenario which explores how our future wellbeing, societal norms, and behaviors might be impacted by the pandemic and new technologies.

Nowhere to Hide in 2025

Gina Clifford—Technology communications manager at Jabil, US
This chapter presents a scenario of life in 2025, when the pandemic threat has passed. But social inequalities of the 2020 pandemic are more pervasive than ever. As a digital platform designed to keep us safe is now required by governments, not everyone feels safer and, for some people, there is nowhere to hide.

PART 5: SECTORAL FUTURES

Insurance in the Post-Pandemic World

David Smith—Futurist and chief executive, Global Futures and Foresight, UK

For insurers, the pandemic has dramatically accelerated their need to embrace digitalization. This was already a highly disruptive trend prior to the virus but is now essential for their survival. It goes far beyond remote working and requires a change in not just technology but also the organizations' culture, processes, and propositions.

Collectively Producing Zero-Waste Food: Zainab's Scenario in 2025

Dr. Nisreen Lahham—Regional project manager for Wastewater Reuse in the MENA in Egypt

This chapter uses scenario thinking to explore the possible implications of the pandemic on our future food security. It examines the issue of food security in light of restricted food imports and disconnected supply chains. In this context, the responses we could make are discussed along with an examination of how these responses could shape a new revolutionary scenario for the agricultural sector.

Five Technologies Shaping the Post-Pandemic Future of Food

Tony Hunter—Global futurist and foresight strategy consultant specializing in the future of food, Australia

The pandemic has irrevocably changed our world. But what might be the legacy of the pandemic for the food, beverage, and agri-food industries, and the very future of food? This chapter argues that in crisis there's opportunity and we need to make the most of this one and use technology to fundamentally change our food system.

Post-Pandemic Urban Mobility: A Tale of Three Regions
Boyd Cohen, Ph.D.—Co-founder and CEO of Iomob, Spain
The trillion-dollar question for those of us in the global mobility ecosystem is what regulatory, economic, and behavioral changes might we see when we have passed the Covid-19 pandemic? It is too simple to project one future on the world when the trends prior to the crisis and the attitudes and orientations of different regions in the world toward mobility have been on very different trajectories? Boyd posits that in the developed world, we could see three different possible paths for urban mobility emerge post-pandemic from West to East.

The Reinvention of Travel–and Residency
Hjörtur Smárason—CEO, Visit Greenland
The tourism sector was one of the hardest hit by the pandemic. While the sector in general is expected to recover by 2024 or 2025, many fear it may never return to the same patterns as before. The tourism sector that rises from the ashes could be very different with changed demand patterns, behaviors, and products. This chapter explores key forces shaping the emerging future of travel and argues that the prospects for sectoral growth may not change significantly until truly commercially viable electric airlines emerge and spread their wings.

Post-Pandemic Public Education: Four Scenarios for the United States
Jason Siko, Ph.D.—Instructional technology consultant for Wayne Regional Educational Service Agency, US
This chapter examines the interplay between two factors that will have a strong influence on the post-pandemic future of public education in the US, the economy, and public sentiment. In the context of an impending recession exacerbated by the pandemic and the recent presidential election, four scenarios are outlined for public education based on the speed of the economic recovery and possible shifts in the US political landscape.

Principal's Morning Announcement—Public School 3.16, Brooklyn, New York, September 1st, 2025

Alisha Bhagat—Futurist and senior strategist at Forum for the Future, US
This vision of the future is inspired by the school closures impacting students in New York City. Starting March 16th, 2020, NYC schools shut down and moved millions of students, parents, and teachers to remote learning. This scenario explores the potential lasting impacts on school life as we adapt to living with the virus.

After the Pause: The Unspoken Futures of Post-Pandemic Higher Education

Alexandra Whittington—Global futurist, writer, and faculty member on the futures program at the University of Houston, US
This chapter offers future scenarios for higher education founded on wild cards, black swans, and surprises that could take hold in the post-pandemic period. The future of higher education is complicated and interwoven with a number of other variables; therefore, the aim is to offer us insights into the potential impacts of important possible future shocks in the aftermath of the pandemic.

PART 6: INNOVATION AND TECHNOLOGY

Beyond the Pandemic—All Change

Roger Camrass—Founder and director of research at CIONET UK and visiting professor at the University of Surrey, UK
This chapter explores how the pandemic could lead to an acceleration in the rate of change, projecting us decades forward in the evolution of the digital world.

Crisis (危機) = Danger (危) + Opportunity (機): A New Renaissance

José Cordeiro—Director of the Millennium Project, Spain
The pandemic represents a global danger that uncovers a great opportunity for innovation in the middle of this planetary crisis. This

chapter argues that, in the next ten years, we are going to see more technological changes than in the last 100 years and more advances in the following decade than in the previous century.

How the Pandemic Has Become an Accelerant for Virtual Presence

Cathy Hackl—Futurist and business strategist, Cathy Hackl LLC, US
The future of communications and connection has a lot to do with the concept of presence and the convergence of both the physical and virtual worlds. This convergence will create new opportunities, and challenges.

How Digital Ecosystems Might Shape the Post-Pandemic Recovery

Greg Wasowski—Senior principal, ISV Industry Solutions Technology Strategy, Salesforce, UK
This chapter presents a view of how partner ecosystems might evolve in the near future and explores the importance of empathy, agility, trust and transparency, and resilience.

From Surviving to Thriving the Pandemic: Digital Transformation in Action for Connected Communities

Reza Jafari—Chairman, CEO, and founder of e-Development International, US
A connected communities ecosystem platform can play a significant role in the creation and advancement of collaborative innovation and citizen engagement. This chapter offers a framework of actions at the intersection of technology, economics, and humanity that could enhance collective contributions and the sharing of outcomes.

A Viridian Aurora

Frederic Balmont—Work inspector, Ministry of Labour, France
The virus awakens our aspiration for equality, certainties flicker, new values emerge, then resistance, riots, and solutions. This chapter argues that the key to our future lies in our approach to technology and ecology. By revealing our potentialities as well as our dead ends, this crisis

presents us with a dramatic alternative: a second Age of Enlightenment or the collapse of civilization.

CONCLUSION: FUTURE FRAMEWORKS

Framework 1: Grand Challenges–Emerging Global Opportunities and Critical Risks

Rohit Talwar—Global futurist and CEO, Fast Future, UK

This chapter provides a practical checklist of emerging opportunities and potential risks across five key domains: economy and finance; government and governance; individuals and society; science and technology; and sustainability, energy, and environment.

Framework 2: The Technology Timeline–Advances Shaping the Next Decade

Rohit Talwar—Global futurist and CEO, Fast Future, UK
Karolina Dolatowska—Foresight researcher and business manager, Fast Future, UK

As we prepare for the next waves of change, what are the critical technologies we need to have on our radar and potentially develop a deeper understanding of? This chapter sets out a comprehensive categorization of critical technology developments that could emerge into the marketplace over three key time horizons—*the next two years; two to five years; and five to ten years and beyond.*

Framework 3: Navigating the Future–50 Critical Questions

Rohit Talwar—Global futurist and CEO, Fast Future, UK
Karolina Dolatowska—Foresight researcher and business manager, Fast Future, UK

The core insights and messages from across the book are distilled into 50 critical questions for individuals, civil society leaders, businesses, investors, and governments as they seek to understand the forces shaping the decade ahead and start to map out their preferred paths to the future.

20 Shifts on the Path to 2030

By Rohit Talwar

What are some of the emerging future factors that could turn into influential shifts shaping the next decade and beyond?

This book provides a broad scan of the horizon for some of the critical future factors that might shape our world over the next five to ten years and beyond. The contributors discuss a number of megatrends, clearly identifiable sub-trends, and emerging ideas that we already believe will have some influence on the scenarios that could play out. In this chapter we take a look beyond those strong drivers of change to look at some of the rapidly evolving developments and weaker signals of possible change that could turn into major societal shifts quite rapidly.

These factors are grouped under operating environment, lives and lifestyles, economy, and business and technology. Many of the future factors highlighted below have a close relationship to the United Nations' 17 Sustainable Development Goals (SDGs).[1] Hence, at the core of much of the discussion below is the question: how committed are we as a planet to delivering on these goals and delivering sustainable lifestyle advances for all citizens?

Operating Environment

1. Accelerated Responses to Climate Change and Eco Tipping Points

How might growing awareness of the scale of the climate crisis raise awareness and encourage action on the broader set of environmental challenges facing the planet?

The climate crisis has started to focus people's attention on a wider set of critical planetary boundaries that are being reached or exceeded. There is a growing sense and awareness that the levels of response from organizations, nations, and individuals need to be scaled up and accelerated to bring the planet back from the brink and that the natural environment doesn't negotiate or care about treaties, agreements, or targets. This in turn is driving increased understanding that action on a massive scale is required to address a broader range of challenges beyond dangerous climate change, such as forest fires, desertification, loss of biodiversity, declining air quality, and contamination of ground water.

Climate change remains the primary focal point for most, but actions to address it could bring wider ecological benefits. The evidence driving the need for a deeper response is increasingly incontrovertible. For example, the latest and most comprehensive report from the United Nations Intergovernmental Panel on Climate Change[2] warns that global warming could reach or exceed 1.5 degrees Celsius above pre-industrial levels within two decades. Breaking these thresholds could lead to irreversible damage from catastrophic weather events, melting of polar ice, rising sea levels, and flooding.

Estimates for tackling these ecosystem challenges over the next two decades range from US$300 billion to US$50 trillion[3] and 1-5% of GDP annually for different countries. The stark reality of the situation is that nations and the global community will be faced with tough choices. Decisions will be required over whether to prioritize planetary protection or accept the costs to the planet, to nations, to economies, to lives, and to livelihoods of limited and insufficient action. Action is already being scaled up in some areas, for example, there is a clear acceleration in the rate at which nations, cities, and businesses are bringing forward their timescales for reaching net zero in three key domains, namely carbon emissions, non-recyclable or reusable waste, and energy consumption from the grid. Rising public awareness is also driving a greater consideration of ecological factors and sustainability in individual purchasing decisions and lifestyle choices.

2. Uncharted Territory for Globalism

What new models, structures, and approaches might we need for collective action to tackle current and emerging global challenges?

The pandemic, numerous points of diplomatic tension, and the digital reshaping of global commerce have highlighted serious limitations in existing global governance models and frameworks. Clear fault lines have emerged or become more pronounced in fields ranging from conflict resolution and national and global governance, through to international trade, regulation of corporate power, and monetary and fiscal policy.

The capacity of nations, global institutions, economic alliances, and regulatory regimes to respond and adapt to these shifts will be key. They will determine and regulate the level of volatility globally and be key determinants in the frequency, duration, and depth of national and global shocks, recessions, and depressions. While there are many interesting discussions taking place, few have led to genuinely scalable experiments that could result in new models, institutional structures, and approaches that could serve for a decade or more.

3. System Resilience

How can we learn critical lessons from the pandemic and develop better response mechanisms and greater resilience across core societal systems and infrastructures?

The pandemic has highlighted huge variations in the capacity of nations and global mechanisms to respond to an all-encompassing crisis. The coming years could see an increased incidence of such low probability, high impact "wild card" events. From natural disasters and failures caused by human error and oversight, through to overloading of critical systems, and deliberately malicious actions, the register of potential risks continues to grow.

Events that could drive potentially critical failures and breakdowns range from pandemics, severe climate impacts, and sunstrikes, through to infrastructure failures, societal unrest, and the collapse or overthrow of political regimes. They could equally result from the actions of states and non-state actors in the form of large-scale hacking, use of bioweapons, and conventional terrorist actions to disrupt essential services and infrastructure.

The societal impacts will be determined by government, business, and individual choices over the level of resource allocation and capacity building to handle the prevention, detection, response management, and outcome mitigation of such events. The challenge will be for nations to overcome pride and arrogance to learn from the strategies, response protocols, and practical reactions of the nations that have done best in responding to the pandemic.

4. Conflict Resolution

What approaches could prove most effective for resolving national and international tensions in a post-pandemic world?
Tension levels around the world appear to be rising, while the economic stability of many fragile nations is at risk. The dramatic collapse of the Afghan government and return to power of the Taliban highlights how quickly situations can evolve and create new potential sources of national, regional, and international tension and turbulence.

Economic and environmental imperatives are also increasing the potential for conflict over ownership of, and access to, water, land, minerals, and other natural resources. The opportunity here will be to find modern era approaches to conflict resolution. Indeed, as the capability of artificial intelligence (AI) advances, there may even be the potential for technology mediated solutions.

Lives and Lifestyles

5. *Corporatization of Housing, Home Ownership, and the Rise of the Rental Society*

How desirable and achievable would it be to shift from ownership to rental across key areas of human activity?

There has been a rapid growth in the corporatization of the housing market in the US in particular, with 200+ US financial institutions buying low end and entry level properties and entire towns across America. The underlying assumption is that people's financial situation may well change for the worse in the coming years through a combination of economic instability and job replacement through technology. This is not a uniquely US phenomenon and could turn into a global trend or megatrend within the space of a few years.

In the face of potentially long-term unemployment and resulting economic hardship, those affected would then be forced to sell their properties and switch to renting. Of course, in many countries, renting has been the only option as property prices are prohibitively high. This trend ties in with a broader view that the rise of the rental and sharing economy will continue over the next two decades—to the point where most of us own little or nothing and rent everything, from our homes to the clothes on our back. Key questions here are whether such shifts would be welcomed or opposed by society and whether this would lead to more or less financial freedom and security.

6. *Compassion v Competition*

Can we influence whether compassion or competition become the more dominant driver of individual priorities and behaviors in the coming decade?

The pandemic has highlighted even more starkly and exacerbated major societal challenges around the world—from extreme poverty and homelessness to acute mental health issues and wide geographical differences in health and life expectancy. The question now arises over how different nations will respond to these challenges. Some have suggested that this is a time for extreme compassion and the use of taxation to fund enhanced social care programs and guaranteed basic incomes (GBI).

In contrast, many argue that the costs of caring for those left behind is a burden on society and a drain on resources. The suggestion here is that the best way forward is to encourage self-sufficiency, competition, and the survival of the healthiest, smartest, most adaptable, and most productive. Others point out that, in many respects, the latter is already happening and that societal divides will be harder to close and are more likely to widen. An overt decision to move in either direction will require tough choices and extreme bravery for the governments involved.

7. Generational Conflict

How might the shifts shaping society play out in the relationships between generations?

A number of factors are contributing to the potential for increasing tensions between generations. Examples would include changing family and relationship structures, the declining potential for home ownership, and the rapid evolution of the technology and social platforms that provide the operating context in which different generations connect. In many countries there are concerns that those under 25 may be the first groups in society to earn and save less than their parents.

At the same time, the data suggests that young people are increasingly turning to the crypto economy to manage their finances and achieve far higher returns than the more traditional saving and investment routes favored by older generations. While there is the potential to experience massive losses, there are also many examples of new crypto investors achieving higher returns within days on one small investment than their parents have earned in a lifetime.

In the world of work, rapidly evolving workplace environments and the growth of working from home have created wide differences in the nature of the employment experience of new entrants to the labor market compared to their parents. Workplace automation and the rise of AI are also causing challenges in both directions. Older generations are finding it ever harder to secure new opportunities with equivalent rewards to the jobs they have been automated out of. For young people, accelerating automation is creating opportunity and also the risk of shorter employment tenure. How generations can be brought closer together will be a defining challenge of the next decade, with many questioning whether it is even desirable.

8. AI Society

Where could the rise of AI have the greatest impacts across society and how can we prepare people for what's coming?

There is much talk about the potential of AI. However, understanding is lagging on what it is, how it works, and the potential breadth and depth of its penetration and transformational impact across every aspect of human activity. Examples range from autonomous vehicles, the organization of personal finances, and career development through to management of our health and the matching of potential partners on dating apps.

Some nations like Finland have a conscious commitment to raise citizens' AI literacy through the free Elements of AI[4] online education tool. However, the majority of nations are currently doing little to encourage citizen awareness or participation in the debate about the role we want AI to play in our societies.

9. Humanity 2.0

Are human enhancement and life extension desirable and how can we ensure they don't increase and entrench divides across society?

Reality is beginning to catch up with the science fiction around the use of scientific and technological advances to change how we define what it means to be human. Growing levels of funding are being directed toward enhancing ourselves and the pursuit of transhuman capabilities. The domain encompasses developments such as radical life extension and the augmentation of basic human capabilities through genetic, chemical, bio-mechanical, and electronic enhancements.

The field has many passionate advocates who believe this is the logical next step in our evolution. There are many in the opposing corner who argue that this is unnatural, conveys an unfair advantage on those who could afford such enhancements, and would further deepen existing divides between the haves and have nots.

The implications of such developments are wide ranging, from influencing workplace rewards and career advancement opportunities through to allocation of residence permits and student grading in education. How regulators navigate this minefield could have a significant bearing on the future of the evolution of the augmentation sector and in the competition between nations with differing views on the social and financial benefits of augmentation.

Economy

10. Single Global Currency

Could a single currency be workable and how might we manage the transition and governance processes?

If we look 30-100 years ahead, in a digitally centric world, it is hard to imagine the planet operating with multiple state issued fiat currencies. The rise of the crypto economy offers the potential for multiple digital currencies and tokens to exist in parallel. However, it is highly possible to envisage one digital currency being accepted globally as the base medium of exchange through which all citizens can be rewarded and make their purchases. Clearly, there are questions about how quickly this might happen, how it would work, governance, and which currency would be chosen. The most likely candidate today would be a so-called "stablecoin" that was initially pegged to the value of a key global currency such as the US Dollar, Chinese Yuan, or Euro.

The core challenges of such a development would include how to manage nations' transitions from their fiat currencies and addressing citizen concerns over the potential for all their financial activities to be monitored and judged by governments. A further issue would be the potential for the strongest economic powers to influence the governance of the currency and the issuance of new coins. Today, governments can print or borrow money to address financial challenges such as paying for the economic costs of addressing the pandemic. Such policy options might be less possible with a single global currency.

11. Infrastructure and Growth

How can we deliver the global infrastructure required to enable sustainable growth and development for all?

The role of infrastructure is well understood in enabling growth, particularly in developing countries. Highway systems alone are seen to enable anything up to 20% of the GDP for different countries. Estimates suggest that total investment of US$100 trillion[5] or more could be required over the next three decades to deliver a modern, robust, and resilient physical infrastructure of roads, rail, airports, ports, and energy facilities. Providing high speed broadband connections and associated infrastructure could add a further US$2 trillion[6] to this figure.

The costs of delivery vary dramatically across the planet and many of those most in need of infrastructure are least able to pay for it and deliver the financial returns required by investors. Hence, there are the twin challenges of developing innovative and equitable new infrastructure funding models and transforming the cost of delivery. Smart and self-healing materials, 3D printing, rapid construction, robotic assembly, embedded monitoring sensors, and modular scalable architectures are all seen as potential contributors to the solution.

12. Wealth, Taxes, and Resource Allocation

How might we bring about a rebalancing of rising global disparities in wealth, incomes, asset distribution, and resource ownership, and how desirable is it to address the challenge?

Research from Oxfam suggests that in 2018 just 26 billionaires had as much wealth as the 3.8 billion poorest people on the planet, roughly 50% of the population.[7] A 2020 Oxfam report found that the world's 2,153 billionaires had more wealth collectively than 4.6 billion people who made up 60% of global population.[8] Numerous studies have also found that the income gap is rising in many countries.

Mechanisms exist to bring about a more equitable distribution of financial resources. For example, taxation of wealth and incomes has traditionally been a core policy tool to redistribute resources across society. However, the last 40-50 years have seen increasing competition between nations to bring down personal and corporate tax rates, with the aim of attracting the wealthiest and increasing inward investment. In parallel, there has been a growing concern that the amount of tax actually paid by corporations has declined and is hard to address without coordinated global action.

As mentioned earlier, opinions are divided over whether redistribution is even a desirable policy goal. Measures such as introducing GBI proved popular to help populations through the worst impacts of the pandemic. However, while a number of experiments are taking place, there is also ideological opposition in many quarters to the adoption of a more permanent GBI solution.

13. The Crypto Economy

What key impacts could the rise of the crypto economy have on the economic landscape and the management of personal finances?

In just 13 years we have seen the crypto market rise to a market capitalization of over US$2 trillion at its peak in May of 2021. Starting with Bitcoin, a range of crypto assets have emerged utilizing blockchain as the core enabling technology for distributed and decentralized applications that cannot be controlled by any one entity. Of particular interest is the notion of smart contracts that allow transactions to be completed without any human involvement, thus enabling the emergence of decentralized autonomous organizations (DAOs) with no employees and governance controlled by the holders of the relevant crypto tokens.

The sheer scale of the opportunity is seeing market entry of large financial institutions, with a growing number of corporations adding crypto assets to their balance sheets and developing their own crypto token solutions. Countries like El Salvador are adopting Bitcoin as legal tender, and others like China and Ghana are piloting central bank digital currencies (CBDCs).

With an estimated 300 million+ global users,[9] the field is still in its infancy. Concerns remain over the unregulated nature of the market, volatility, and the potential for fraud and manipulation. The largely tech-savvy crypto community have high hopes of disrupting the traditional financial system, helping take people out of poverty across the planet, and creating a fairer and more transparent marketplace for investments, savings, loans, and more complex products. Corporations, financial institutions, and governments in particular are torn by the desire to participate in and influence the development of the crypto economy while also worrying about the loss of control and the threat to their franchises.

14. Smart Money

What opportunities might arise from the digitization of money and the incorporation of intelligent functionality into our mediums of exchange?
The digitization of money is opening up a range of new possibilities around how we can build intelligence into currency. Even without the rise of the crypto economy, we are seeing a gradual shift toward smarter money. Examples that are emerging, or on the near horizon, include user designed savings products; rounding up our purchases, such as our daily coffee, to invest in savings, equities, and crypto; companies replacing loyalty points with savings plans if you buy their offerings; increasingly smart money and credit card trading our purchase history for discounts and rewards; and turning our social media likes into assets with a transactional value.

Business and Technology

15. Rapidly Changing Reality

How might the nature of business, work, and the workplace evolve and the expectations and responsibilities of employers change?
The next decade could see the business environment and the nature of business experience an unprecedented level and pace of change. Several factors will come together with secondary and tertiary outcomes that we cannot even conceive of from where we stand today. Businesses are already being challenged to think about the purpose, social role, and wider societal responsibility of for-profit organizations.

From taxation policy and profit sharing through to environmental, social, and corporate governance (ESG), societal and government expectations could rise dramatically. New organizational forms and collaborative structures and ecosystems could proliferate. The debate about how to measure corporate performance and contribution could evolve, with regulation driving an emphasis shift from shareholder returns to wider stakeholder contribution.

Within the workplace, pandemic disruption led organizations to put a greater emphasis on self-directed learning and development. This has been accompanied by accelerated job rotation, automated onboarding processes, and deepening of the autonomy and level of virtual connectivity within teams. Virtual working has changed organizational cultures and the process of socializing new employees. The role of managers has also been put under the spotlight, highlighting the difference between those who make a real value adding contribution and those who largely attend meetings and read reports.

The next few years are also likely to see many organizations try and reduce their dependency on humans by accelerating the automation process and adoption of AI. This in turn could lead to a decline in the size of workforces, a shift away from teams, and deep technological unemployment as the displaced workforce reskills for new roles. At the same time, the new industries coming through, such as autonomous vehicles, personalized medicine, rapid construction, and synthetic biology, are all highly automated from the start and hence require less employees for each dollar of revenue generated.

Questions are likely to arise over what the responsibility of employers will be toward their displaced employees. To what extent might they still provide access to learning resources and offer continuing training and job seeker support? The level of debate could also increase over whether firms should contribute in some way toward the costs of transitional GBI payments while workers retrain and seek new employment. Could employers one day be asked to take responsibility for ensuring job creation in the economy in proportion to their contribution to GDP? This might be through jobs in supplier organizations, support for new venture incubators, and direct investment and mentoring of startups.

16. Digital Literacy Divide

In an increasingly technology-centric world, how can the acquisition of deep digital literacy be accelerated across society?

Whether in business or in wider society, the reliance on technology is increasing and demanding that we take society-wide digital literacy capabilities to a higher level. Failure to do so could lead to a greater digital divide, with citizens increasingly being locked out of career opportunities, access to services, and financial opportunities. Digital is penetrating every aspect of organizations, with increasingly automated tools for tasks such as workflow management, decision-making, team and task coordination, HR support, productivity monitoring, and communications. Hence, career advancement is increasingly likely to be determined in part by our ability to understand and get the best out of the technologies proliferating in the workplace.

Across society, technology is increasingly governing how we access public services, make purchases, engage with friends and family, and book everything from travel to entertainment. In the personal finance world, many providers are delivering greater functionality online, gradually closing physical branches, and reducing the amount of human telephone support. The world of crypto investment is still largely geared toward the tech-savvy who are willing to do the research to learn how to access the best decentralized finance offerings.

17. New Business Models

How might the range of underlying financial models and pricing options for businesses evolve in a fast changing, digital economy?

A common feature of most crypto ventures is the publication of a white paper that sets out the "Tokenomics"—the underlying economic model for how the business operates. While similar to a pitch deck or business plan for new ventures, the range of models tends to be much wider. In more traditional markets, the notion of alternative business models is starting to take hold. For example, subscription services, gainsharing with suppliers, and "pay for usage" models are becoming increasingly common. New ideas now entering the market include accepting personal advertisements and allowing brands to access our online networks in return for discounts and rental of everything from household goods to clothing. Recycling schemes are also becoming more common where customers can drop off unwanted items, such as clothing, in return for discounts on new or recycled products.

The rise of the crypto economy offers several new models such as paying with crypto currencies, suppliers potentially incorporating capital gainsharing with customers, and issuance of crypto tokens to fund new developments with direct reward distribution from the venture to the token holders. With many brands offering loyalty points, digital models allow for those tokens to be traded more easily, enabling customers to realize the value of relatively small amounts of points held across multiple brands.

18. Recoil from Big—Does Size Matter?

Could the growing power and privacy infringement capabilities of multinational corporates lead to a shift in consumer purchasing toward alternative providers?

Concerns continue to rise about the power of multinationals, their influence over governments and regulators, and their ability to dominate and even manipulate markets. These concerns are amplified by the extent to which these firms are able to invade our privacy with digital technologies, and the potential for "surveillance capitalism" in the exploitation of our personal data. In response, there are weak signals around the world of people opting to buy from alternative providers, which are often more human, independent, local, smaller, and increasingly focused on ethical and sustainable offerings. The rise of social ventures in many markets is further evidence of the growing demand for such alternatives.

19. Closed Corporate Ecosystems

How might digital technologies give rise to new corporate community ecosystems in the crypto economy?

In a world of intense competition where technology innovation effectively drives down prices, corporations will increasingly look for ways of enhancing revenues and profits. Key strategies might include increasing the returns on customer loyalty and lock in, reducing the cost of customer acquisition, and decreasing the share of revenues given to third parties such as retailers and credit card companies. Hence, we are seeing the desire to grow customer bases and networks and binding them in so that a growing proportion of their spend happens within the corporation's ecosystem. Discounts and loyalty rewards can help lock customers in and encourage them to recruit their friends and family.

The use of a corporate crypto token for payment could further incentivize customers. This was seen by many as Facebook's goal when it launched its Libra crypto token (now Diem). The larger the network, the more other vendors are likely to join, thus creating further incentives for customers to do the bulk of their purchasing within the ecosystem. For customers, alongside the loyalty discounts and perks, there is also the potential for appreciation in the value of the crypto currency. While this is a clear development path for the big technology players such as Amazon and Google, it could also become a prime opportunity for brands as diverse as Disney and Walmart.

20. Corporation Zero and the "Designed for Digital" Enterprise
What impact could digital technologies have on the way we think about the design and functioning of our organizations?

The explosion of "born digital" ventures is triggering a wave of new thinking about how we design and run our organizations. The rise of DAOs has also highlighted the potential to create entirely digital entities with literally no employees, no management, and no organizational structure. In response, the coming years could see the rise of "corporation zero" organizational models. In such entities, the start point is to focus on the desired outcomes, the core processes required to deliver them, and the set of measures and indicators needed to assess and optimize performance and achievement of targets.

The requirements can then be modeled in simulations to see what can be done entirely digitally, where physical elements are required such as production equipment and robots, and where human involvement might still be essential. In both cases, the emphasis will be on ensuring that the physical and human elements of the system can feed in the desired information to ensure the effective functioning of the "designed for digital" enterprise. The appropriate underpinning management structure can then be determined. Over time, advances in AI could see further enhancement of the digital ecosystem, with commensurate headcount reductions. While some see this as a shocking and scarily dystopian possibility, others view it as a natural outcome of the rise of digital.

- *Which emerging developments could have the greatest impact on your lives and your organization?*
- *How can we raise societal understanding of current drivers of change and potential shifts on the horizon?*
- *What new models of societal engagement, policy development, and governance might be required to help navigate the next decade at the national and global level?*

Rohit Talwar is a global futurist and the CEO of Fast Future, where he focuses on helping clients explore the emerging future, respond to global opportunities, and identify and manage risks on the horizon.

ECONOMICS AND BUSINESS

Life Next: How Our World Could Change Post-Pandemic

By Marian Salzman

How might this crisis impact businesses, lifestyles, and mindsets?

As I write this, many of us are still sheltering in place or working from home, fearful of how high the infections will rise—and how deep the incursion will be into our lives. Nothing is as important as surviving the crisis, but history has taught us that being forewarned can lead to better outcomes. Here then, are my thoughts on what lies ahead.

What's Next for Work-Life?
- Will soaring office towers be relegated to the past?
- How might we redefine "personal space"?

For much of the last quarter-century, many of us have had a sneaking feeling that screen-based living was a lazier, morally inferior version of real life in the physical realm. The pandemic has reframed that view. Virtual has become vital.

With millions of people—and many businesses—getting their first taste of telecommuting, it's likely we will see a long-term shift toward greater use of remote work. A study by employee visibility software company Prodoscore reported a 47% spike in productivity among its

30,000 US-based user companies in March–April 2020, compared with a year prior. Based on positive experiences with at-home work during the pandemic, a growing number of companies, including Facebook, Twitter, Dell, and Novartis, announced that they will permit most employees to work remotely on a permanent basis.

Professional services moved online, doctors, therapists, and lawyers are now a few keystrokes or thumb taps away from patients and clients. How long before portals start certifying professionals across industries? Could there be value in a "verified by Google" financial consultant or an "Amazon-certified" aesthetician? The question—now we're seeing everything from news to *Saturday Night Live* produced remotely and the US Supreme Court hearing arguments via phone—is: What really needs to take place in person?

Looking ahead, I expect to see fewer temples of commerce built and today's office towers repurposed, perhaps to include community use, with some razed for green spaces. Across public and commercial venues, personal space will be prioritized. Employees who must be at the office, could see more staggered hours working arrangements and a shift away from open-plan. Cattle-car approaches to space optmization in some restaurants and bars could be rejected on a more permanent basis, leading to new norms of more space between tables, stricter crowd size limits in public spaces, and perhaps even upcharges for additional space, akin to paying for extra legroom on flights.

Parkour for Business

- Could a post-pandemic economy revitalize private–public partnerships?
- Might flesh-and-blood employees prove too great a liability in the retail world?

With so much recent focus on agility, it's been fascinating to see who responded to the new normal fastest and best. This could be a good indicator of who's most likely to thrive in our fast-changing world.

Quick-service restaurants such as Subway and Panera Bread became grocery stores, offering staples such as bread, milk, and cheese. Dan

White, president of Ultimate Fighting Championship, secured a private island on which to host televised fights. Other businesses pivoted to produce critical goods. For a period, breweries and distilleries made hand sanitizer. Car manufacturers churned out ventilators. Private–public partnerships and cross-industry collaborations may become a vital component of our rebuilt economies.

Another change could be increased automation. With essential workers at heightened viral risk, has there been a better time for droids and drones to take over? Already, robotic pods such as Nuro, Starship, and Serve deliver goods to homes. Drones now drop off medical supplies and disinfect public spaces. How long before individuals get into the act? After months of online shopping for essentials, it's not hard to picture dispatching one's personal R2-D2 to pick up weekly grocery supplies..

The Future of Home
- Will apartment complexes compete on emergency preparedness?
- Might builders favor cold rooms over wine cellars? Or will we build them ourselves?

Despite lockdown laws, some Airbnb hosts listed their homes as isolated pandemic retreats. In future, look for people to emphasize physical separation when choosing second—and maybe even first—homes. Tiny houses on far-off sites could be hot properties. For those remaining in cities, imagine a future in which apartment complexes compete on emergency preparedness rather than fancy gyms.

The past few years have seen an increasing number of people adopt a bunker mentality, with doomsday preppers at the extreme end of this trend. Not everyone is going to go full-on prepper, but we can expect more stockpiling and emergency preparedness. Already, long-term rations are available at Walmart.

Be it on Main Street or in the mountains, we can expect home-buyers to increasingly favor homes with larger pantries and cellars. Some people might build these units themselves. The pandemic could accelerate the growing trend toward self-sufficiency and DIY, reflected by growth in home vegetable plots. People are pining to feel more connected to nature, envious of the simpler existence of generations past. They want to experience the "real." An intrepid few have gone off grid to eke out a subsistence living on their own. The pandemic had many more take baby steps—learning to bake bread, make soap, or take up practical hobbies like carpentry and raising chickens.

The pandemic heightened these impulses, with retailers struggling to meet demand for flour, yeast, and vegetable seeds. Next, we may see more people learning to take care of things themselves rather than relying on others who may not be there when needed.

A New 3 Cs

Will camaraderie, compassion, and community thrive?

In recent years, many of us have mourned the loss of the central tenets of public discourse: civility, compromise, constraint, and conversation. Now we are seeing the emergence of a different set of Cs: camaraderie, compassion, and community. From New York Governor Andrew Cuomo's exhortations to be "a little bit more loving, a little bit more compassionate," to the 750,000 people who volunteered in the UK to help those in need, signs are everywhere that people are eager to connect with, comfort, and care for their fellow humans.

For all the horror caused by the pandemic, hope shines bright.

- *How might entertainment and hospitality brands evolve their offers to encourage their customers to get dressed and go out?*
- *What might the impact be of new platforms or existing players like Amazon and Google certifying professionals across industries— medical, financial, legal, and more?*
- *Could businesses like restaurants and cinemas follow the airlines and upcharge for additional personal space?*

Marian Salzman is senior vice president, global communications at Philip Morris International. She was named one of the world's top five trendspotters and is a highly-awarded public relations executive.

Blockchain and the Crypto Economy—A Platform for Transformation?

By Rohit Talwar and Kapil Gupta

What are blockchain technology and crypto assets and how might they disrupt government issued fiat currencies and traditional financial services markets?

This chapter introduces the core concepts of blockchain technology and the crypto assets that it enables. The reasons for the rapid growth in interest and associated risks are outlined, along with the limitations of government issued fiat currencies that crypto assets seek to address. The impacts of the pandemic on the crypto marketplace are also discussed. Finally, the potential of the crypto economy to drive a transformation of traditional financial markets is explored.

Unless you have been living as an off-grid hermit, the chances are that you will by now have heard about crypto assets, such as Bitcoin (BTC), and the blockchain technology that enables them. This article is the first of two chapters introducing both concepts and explaining how the pandemic has impacted blockchain adoption and participation in the crypto economy—laying the foundations for an accelerated expansion of both in the future.

The second chapter will look at the types of assets that are emerging, explore the types of applications through which they are shaping the crypto economy, and discuss where they might be headed in the near future.

Why the Interest?

As we outline below and in the next chapter, there a number of current and potential applications and benefits of both blockchain and crypto assets. These assets can broadly be divided into cryptocurrencies that act as a store of value similar to gold, and crypto tokens which have some utility such as enabling their owners to purchase services and assets such as digital collectibles. Both blockchain and crypto assets first came to prominence in 2009 with the launch of Bitcoin as the first cryptocurrency and the popularization of the blockchain distributed technology platform that enables it.

Bitcoin was created in response to the Great Financial Crisis of 2007–08. The founder was Satoshi Nakamoto—an individual or group of people that remains anonymous to this day. The smallest unit of account is one Satoshi. There are 100 million Satoshis to one Bitcoin.

Crypto assets and the wider concept of the crypto economy combine a number of core enablers. The key ones being cryptographic methods for enabling secure data transfer and evolving economic models for financial markets. Other important enablers are user network adoption and expansion theories, game theory, exponential growth in computing capability, and the power of distributed computing and data transmission networks.

The crypto sector has attracted an array of highly skilled talent and innovators from across these fields. They are driven by the excitement of new technological challenges and opportunities, the possibility to create new financial and economic systems, and the potential to generate significant monetary gains. Each new project typically sets out its goals and development roadmap in a white paper which also explains the underlying economic functionality—known as the asset's "tokenomics".

The original goal of Bitcoin's founders was to disrupt the centralized financial system that had caused the crisis. In its place they wanted to create a more transparent, fairer, cheaper, and easily accessible decentralized financial system that allowed even the poorest in society to participate fully. The hope was that their standard of living could be enhanced by giving them access to financial products that had previously been out of reach—such as higher interest rates, near zero transaction costs, and fractional ownership of assets.

By limiting the total amount of Bitcoin that could be issued to 21 million, they were also creating a deflationary currency that was intended to be used as cash for transaction purposes. Since then, the crypto marketplace has evolved, and now the largest single factor driving both individual and corporate adoption has been the rapid appreciation in price and market capitalization since Bitcoin was launched. As the best performing asset class in history when considering performance over any ten-year period, Bitcoin is now considered a store of value like gold.

The total crypto market capitalization was US$192 billion on January 1st, 2020, and it more than trebled from the start of 2021, rising from US$776 billion to achieve a peak in May 2021 of around US$2.5 trillion. Bitcoin is the biggest single cryptocurrency in this market, reaching a peak valuation over that period of just over US$1.1 trillion. These market peaks were followed by a total crypto market decline of over US$1 trillion, and a subsequent recovery, at the time of writing, of 50 to 100% or more depending on the crypto asset. Analysis of transaction data suggests that much of this decline was due to large investors forcing down prices to drive out retail investors and create much cheaper entry points for mass accumulation.

Perhaps the biggest surprise to many of those coming fresh to crypto is that most decisions about Bitcoin's future evolution are proposed, voted on, and implemented by its user community.

Rapid growth has drawn interest across the board and fueled the entry into the crypto market of a range of investment banks, hedge funds, institutional investors, sovereign wealth funds, large individual investors, and exchange traded funds. In addition, firms like

MicroStrategies—the largest corporate investor—have been championing Bitcoin investment in particular.

In February 2021, Tesla announced that it had accumulated US$1.5 billion of Bitcoin on its balance sheet. Many others are beginning to enter the market, with interested corporates typically looking to put 4–7% of their balance sheet into crypto assets. The latest development is the entry of countries, such as El Salvador, Paraguay, Argentina, and Brazil looking to adopt Bitcoin other crypto assets as legal tender or to invest in them. A number of countries such as Ghana are also following the lead of China's Digital Yuan pilot project and are at different stages in preparing to launch pilots of their own central bank digital currency (CBDC).

One of the most significant developments of early 2021 was the appointment of leading crypto authority Professor Gary Gensler as the new chair of the US Securities and Exchange Commission (SEC). Gensler had previously been an investment banker and US Treasury official. Prior to appointment, he was a professor of the Practice of Global Economics and Management at the MIT Sloan School of Management, co-director of MIT's Fintech@CSAIL, and senior advisor to the MIT Media Lab Digital Currency Initiative. This was a clear signal that the US government was now taking the crypto economy seriously—both in terms of its advancement and regulation.

Key Risks and Concerns

Since its launch, there have been concerns that Bitcoin, and now other crypto assets, carry with them multiple risks. Many are similar to those that exist in mainstream financial markets, but they have gained more prominence because of the speed with which the crypto economy has grown. A common concern is that the end user's identity is theoretically untraceable and hence there is potential for use in illegal shadow economy transactions, fraud, money laundering, and tax evasion. However, at some point, most people want to convert their digital currencies back into fiat money, at which point the exchanges can identify the individuals or entities involved.

Currently, most crypto assets are not regulated by any governments, central banks, or financial authorities. A purchase of assets such as cryptocurrencies does not grant the owner the same legal rights as investment in a traditional listed equity. Furthermore, the volatility of crypto prices offers the potential for rapid and massive gains and losses—with stories of people turning US$100 into US$1 million, or vice versa, in a just a few days or weeks.

While most blockchains themselves are considered secure, not all are coded to the same standard and there is the potential for errors and hacking. Crypto exchanges, where you can buy and sell crypto assets, are also open to hacking and illegal withdrawal of users' funds. The most prominent example of this was Mt. Gox—a Japanese crypto exchange, which by early 2014 was handling over 70% of all worldwide Bitcoin transactions.

In February 2014, Mt. Gox filed for bankruptcy protection, announcing the theft of approximately 850,000 Bitcoins belonging to customers and the company; these were valued at US$450 million at the time. Some 200,000 of those Bitcoins have since been traced. The present-day exchanges would argue that they are significantly more secure and there have been few examples of exchange hacks, although there are examples of the founders absconding with users' money.

Another key risk is the phenomena known as "pump and dump" where developers announce the launch of a new token, hype it up to drive the price and then sell their holdings at a peak. This typically leads to a massive dump affecting most investors, with the price never really recovering. A variant of this is the "rug pull" where the developers just walk away with the investors' funds and never actually build the crypto application or asset.

At the macro level, a key concern is that the speed at which the crypto market, project functionality, and tokenomics concepts are evolving far outstrips the capacity of governments, financial authorities, and regulators to keep pace. The risks of a major crypto market crash wiping out most investors is often cited as a key concern. Until 2021, most traditional financial institutions had been publicly resistant to crypto because of the threat that a decentralized model posed to their centralized systems and models. The concept creates the potential for huge disruption and the loss of customers who are willing to take their business elsewhere and accept crypto's risks in pursuit of significantly higher rewards.

At the core of many crypto assets is the role of "miners" who compete to validate transactions for which they are rewarded with new tokens. The energy consumption and emissions of these "proof of work" forms of crypto mining, such as is used for Bitcoin, is often raised as a major barrier to adoption. In response, the industry argues that many of the miners are using spare renewable energy generation that would otherwise be wasted. Many miners are also responding to these concerns by moving to locations where there is an abundant supply of renewable energy. The validation protocols for new crypto assets are also becoming far more energy efficient, with many using alternative models such as "proof of stake."

A final concern is the potential for market manipulation—a phenomena that is not uncommon in traditional markets. Typically this involves large investors acting to drive prices down in order to force out nervous smaller investors. This creates greater liquidity and enables those large investors to buy back in at significantly lower prices. Many leading authorities in the sector believe an example of this is the rapid decline in crypto asset prices that started in the middle of May 2021 and continued for over two months. The transparency of account transactions on blockchains enable "on chain" analysis to see these patterns of behavior. Many also point to what appears to be a coordinated flow of news stories that raised fear, uncertainty, and doubt about the risks of crypto investing.

What is a Blockchain?

Before we can understand the potential of this relatively new field and how it might evolve, it is important to understand what it is and how it differs from traditional centralized systems. Blockchain technology is the underlying platform for most crypto assets. So, what is a blockchain? In simple terms, it is a distributed database or ledger secured using advanced cryptographic methods. There are many different types of blockchain in existence today, each with a slightly different approach to delivering the core functionality, validating transactions, and recording them.

Blockchain transactions are time-stamped and stored in a decentralized immutable "append-only log"—meaning that they cannot be amended or erased by any individual or organization once they have been recorded. So, a key differentiator from centralized financial systems is that blockchain technology enables the transfer of data between the parties involved using a decentralized network where every activity is visible and verifiable. While we cannot see the personal details of the counterparties in any transaction, such as a purchase or savings deposit, we can see all the details of the counterparty digital wallet addresses, what happened, and the amounts involved.

Using a decentralized distributed ledger means that each transaction is replicated on every node of the network. All activity on a public blockchain, such as Bitcoin, is transparent and visible to anyone with an Internet connection...and perhaps a little knowledge of where to look. These characteristics provide total transparency, which avoids the need for trust in a centralized organization such as a bank—leading to the notion of a "trustless" and censorship resistant system.

Many proponents of the technology believe it could provide the foundations for a successor to the Internet and revolutionize the design and operations of organizations, the execution of activity across a range of sectors, and the functioning of markets and the global economy. Such massive claims have been met with wild excitement by some who are motivated by the potential for greater efficiency and transparency or even fundamental system changes.

However, there are still high levels of skepticism, concerns over the potential for overhyping, fear around the loss of central control, and questions around the implications of greater transparency. In some quarters, there is also deep resistance to the disruption of markets and the existing order of things. Should the ambitions of blockchain pioneers be fulfilled, there is potential for the shifting of power to a new breed of innovators. As stated earlier, they are typically driven by the desire to use technology to its fullest extent to remove inefficiencies, redistribute wealth, and tackle some of the planet's grandest challenges, while also securing commercial rewards.

The Emergence of Smart Contracts

A core blockchain enabled concept is that of "Smart Contracts." These allow business functionality to be executed without any human interaction or the need for any intermediary. Hence, if an individual wanted to participate in a corporate loan syndication exercise, a complex derivatives trade, or a simple savings deposit, they can do so directly and almost as easily as buying a film ticket on a mobile phone. The entire process is automated using a smart contract and, when the transaction is completed, the funds are automatically transferred without any human interaction.

So, for example, in a property purchase, once the smart contract is satisfied that each of the required legal and procedural steps have been completed and the funds deposited in trust, the contract would automatically transfer the asset to the buyer and place the funds in the seller's account.

The Rise of Decentralized Autonomous Organizations

The decentralized nature of blockchain allows for the underlying functionality and governance of applications to be democratized. For example, the technology has enabled the emergence of so-called "Decentralized Autonomous Organizations (DAOs)." These allow for the user community to decide on the strategy and the direction a project is going in, including proposing, voting on, and implementing any software changes.

A key feature of many DAOs is that, once built, they are run in a completely autonomous way with no employees. This has huge potential impacts for the redesign of existing organizations, employment levels, retraining of the workforce, social security costs, and the broader transition of society to a truly digital environment.

As we can see, blockchain has the potential to transform the efficiency, transparency, cost, and speed of transactions in a whole range of activities across society. The pandemic has allowed people more time to invest in understanding blockchain and crypto assets and thus helped to accelerate learning, interest, and adoption.

What are Cryptocurrencies and Digital Gold?

Cryptocurrencies such as Bitcoin—the largest by market capitalization—are currently the most common application (or use case) for blockchain technology. At the most basic level, Bitcoin aims to provide a decentralized digital form of stored value. This is similar to the way in which gold and silver are used as physical stores of value and a hedge against inflation. Hence, Bitcoin is increasingly referred to as "digital gold."

A key feature and driver of the stored value concept is scarcity. The maximum total supply of Bitcoin is limited to 21 million, with new coins issued to the "miners" who validate and record all transactions conducted across the network. The issuance of new Bitcoins is expected to continue until around the year 2140.

The use case for Bitcoin has evolved rapidly since its launch in 2009. After the initial novelty of using it to buy items such as pizzas, in recent years it has been seen more as a digital store of value. This makes it a potential hedge against the volatility of fiat currencies, in the same manner as precious metals like gold and silver have been used over thousands of years. This move from being seen as a currency to a store of value is predominantly down to its limited supply, the rapid increase in Bitcoin's valuation, and the high volatility in its price.

As more institutional money pours into Bitcoin, and mainstream adoption by companies and countries accelerates, as seen recently in El Salvador, we may see Bitcoin being treated as a currency again in the future. The all-time highest value for one Bitcoin was US$64,804 on April 14th, 2021. Estimates of its future value range from zero to US$1 million within the next five years.

Core Components of the Crypto Economy—Assets and Applications

The term crypto economy extends beyond Bitcoin and covers both assets and applications. Examples of both are presented below. The most commonly known crypto assets and applications are summarized below and described in more detail in the following chapter:

Cryptocurrencies–A digital monetary asset like Bitcoin (BTC)—used as a store of value, a means to purchase goods and services, and as legal tender.

Central Bank Digital Currencies (CBDCs)–Digital versions of fiat currencies such as China's Digital Yuan and the proposed US Dollar CBDC. The goal is to streamline transaction processes, cut costs, improve social inclusion, and reduce the potential for illegal financial activities such as money laundering.

City Coins–Fund raising tools such as MiamiCoin, which are designed to raise funds to support city investments while also delivering returns to the coin holders.

Platforms–These are technology platforms such as Ethereum (ETH) that use a variety of different blockchain designs to create the core functionality used by others to build Decentralized Applications (Dapps)—such as the providers of Decentralized Finance (DeFi) products.

Stablecoins–Asset-backed cryptocurrencies such as Tether (USDT). These aim to maintain the same value over time by tying themselves to a conventional asset like gold or the US Dollar.

Utility Tokens–These are usually issued by applications that run on top of a blockchain like Ethereum—such as the VeChain (VET) supply chain management solution.

Social / Personal Tokens–Tokens typically issued and controlled by individuals such as celebrities and influencers (e.g. Katy Perry) to enable their followers and members to purchase a range of (often exclusive) branded goods and services.

Community Tokens–Tokens typically issued and controlled by a community, network, group, (e.g. $JAMM) and in some cases managed by a decentralized autonomous organization (DAO).

Corporate / Brand / Ecosystem Tokens–Issued by companies to enable their customers, followers, and wider ecosystem to buy goods and services from the brand and reward them with tokens (e.g. Facebook Diem, Dance) as a form of loyalty points.

Security Tokens–These are a digital or "tokenized" form of traditional assets such as securities and options that already have a market value.

Asset / Commodity Tokens–These tokens facilitate the trading of physical real-world assets, which are often regulated commodities like oil or carbon.

Privacy Coins– A category of cryptocurrencies, such as Dash (DASH), which enable anonymous private blockchain transactions, obscuring both their origin and destination addresses.

Meme Coins–These are coins like Dogecoin (Doge) which generally have no specific utility but gain popularity quickly by spreading their message through social media.

The range of applications for which these assets might be used would include:

Decentralized Finance (DeFi)–Blockchain technology has enabled the establishment of an ever-growing number of decentralized "Automated Market Makers" such as PancakeSwap (CAKE), offering a range of products from savings and loans to derivatives and liquidity pools.

Blockchain Enabled Decentralized Supply Chains–Applications range from monitoring the flow and provenance of goods from producer to market, through to the funding of agricultural smallholders.

Non-Fungible Tokens (NFTs)–The creation of a range of uniquely identified digital assets ranging from an educational qualification certificate or the deeds to a property through to limited edition digital collectibles such as artworks, music, and sports memorabilia.

Content Distribution Using Blockchain–Decentralized social media platforms like LBRY.com that allow users to own and monetize their own content such as videos.

Decentralized Artificial Intelligence (AI)–Platforms such as Singu-larityNET that enable end users to select and integrate modules to build their own AI applications.

New Payment Methods–Business models that allow customers to pay using crypto assets and then gainshare with the vendor should the value of the crypto asset appreciate compared to the original purchase price in the underlying fiat currency.

The emergence of new crypto assets and applications is only likely to accelerate in the coming years if the growth of interest, adoption, investment, and development is to be taken as a guide.

Fiat Currency Issues

Unlike government issued fiat money, which can be printed, has an unlimited supply, and is inflationary in nature, i.e. its value decreases over time, Bitcoin's limited supply of 21 million coins is seen to make it more valuable, or deflationary, over time. It is not uncommon for Bitcoins to get lost because people lose the private "key" to access the secure digital wallets in which users hold their cryptocurrencies. Hence, those coins are permanently removed from the money supply.

As a result, once all 21 million Bitcoins have been mined (issued), the total circulating supply will decrease over time. So, Bitcoins will become increasingly rare and potentially more valuable. This feature of increasing value over time is what leads to Bitcoin being considered a deflationary asset and is driving the interest in its adoption by countries—particularly those pandemic-ravaged nations with more fragile currencies and high domestic inflation rates.

A Bitcoin purchased in 2020 will buy you more in 2021, while the buying power of an equivalent initial value in dollars will have declined. Many cryptocurrencies have similar deflationary limits on the total number of coins to be issued, while others deliberately "burn" coins on a regular basis—permanently removing them from circulation.

For countries like El Salvador, the adoption of cryptocurrencies as legal tender is seen as potentially transformative for the nation and its people. Some countries have already used the appreciation in value of their crypto holdings to pay down significant chunks of their national debt. In El Salvador, Bitcoin will be used as legal tender—both as a store of value and as a day-to-day trading currency. Indeed, it is being made compulsory for larger vendors to accept it. There is of course debate over whether people will want to use an appreciating asset like Bitcoin to make everyday purchases.

The government is giving each citizen an initial US$30 of Bitcoin to facilitate the transition away from the dollar and providing a downloadable crypto wallet in which to hold these and any other crypto assets that a citizen might acquire. El Salvador's President Nayib Bukele has appeared on television on numerous occasions to explain the shift to Bitcoin to citizens and even demonstrated how easy it is to download and set up the wallet.

Impact of the Pandemic

The 2020 pandemic saw a massive growth of interest in, and adoption of, cryptocurrencies in particular. This was helped by a significant fall in the price of crypto assets—mirroring the collapse of global stock markets. Other enabling factors were people having more free time and potentially more disposable income as a result of lockdowns with much of the world effectively being shut down.

A growth in free time helped drive the rise in adoption of newer social media applications like TikTok, Clubhouse, Telegram, and Discord. This in turn led to these being used as both education platforms and a means of building large communities around specific assets and crypto influencers. This rising user interest and willingness to invest, backed by a growing social media crypto ecosystem, also drove the accelerated development of a range of more functional blockchain applications in fields like Decentralized Finance (DeFi).

Evolution of the Crypto Ecosystem

The cryptocurrency ecosystem is evolving very rapidly. There are over 8,000 cryptocurrencies and tokens currently listed on Coinmarketcap.com—which is considered the most comprehensive global crypto price and market information platform. This growth reflects the growing range of possible uses of blockchains and cryptocurrencies—from stores of value and digital collectibles through to applications with specific DeFi functionality.

In many cases, firms are issuing crypto coins or tokens to fund the launch and expansion of their business—in the same way as some might look to raise equity funding. A key difference is that crypto assets can often be used to buy services from the underlying company. Other important differences are that crypto assets do not convey legal rights in the same way as equities, and most are unregulated even though they are traded on public exchanges.

A feature that makes crypto assets popular is that fractional ownership is much easier than with equities. For example, traditionally it has been quite difficult to find a broker willing to offer fractional ownership of an Amazon share valued at over US$3,000. The transaction fees have also made it prohibitive to invest very small amounts. However, with just ten dollars, many crypto exchanges will allow you to buy a fraction of a Bitcoin or other crypto assets.

Key to the adoption of cryptocurrencies is the concept of "network effects"—where a product becomes more valuable as more people use it, with the potential for exponential growth as adoption rates accelerate. Hence, it is not necessarily a superior technology that defines success, but the levels of adoption and usage. The social media channels have played an important part in educating the growing crypto user base and building communities around specific crypto assets.

The total number of unique cryptocurrency users globally is hard to determine as individuals may have their coins stored in more than one wallet and so the number of unique wallet addresses is not a reliable indicator. At the time of writing in 2021, estimated worldwide user numbers range from around 200 million to the 300 million suggested by TripleA, a blockchain company based out of Singapore. The majority of these are identified as being at graduate level or above. India is believed to have the largest user base, with some estimating it to have around 100 million crypto holders.

The adoption rate for cryptocurrencies is currently at a roughly similar point to where the Internet was in 1997. Many believe that the transition from the current level to one billion users could be even faster than the 7.5 years it took the Internet to reach that milestone. For many, the shift to mass market adoption and widespread participation is the most exciting possibility, as it offers the potential to lift people out of poverty and transform lives and prospects across the planet.

Conclusion—A Transformational Tipping Point?
In the analysis so far, we have focused on explaining the functionality, applications, and perceived benefits of blockchain technology and crypto assets. From the outline above, what is already clear is that they are evolving rapidly, the full range of possibilities and implications is as yet unknowable, and while there are obvious risks, there is the potential for truly transformational impact across global society.

In the next chapter we will explore some of the possible applications and evolution paths.

- *What has been your experience of blockchain and crypto assets to date and what are the factors that could determine business and individual engagement with them in the future?*

- *What would it take to see wider acceptance of cryptocurrencies as a legitimate challenger to fiat money and a sustainable store of value?*
- *What impact could increasing adoption of cryptocurrencies by countries have on their financial stability and on the global economy?*

Rohit Talwar is a global futurist and the CEO of Fast Future, where he focuses on helping clients explore the emerging future, respond to global opportunities, and identify and manage risks on the horizon.

Kapil Gupta is a technology and crypto analyst, commentator, enthusiast, and investor. He is a transformational coach to business executives and entrepreneurs and the founder of Nibana.life. Kapil is a TEDx speaker with an MBA from the University of Edinburgh Business School and an undergraduate degree in Computer Systems from the Open University of British Columbia. He is a co-author of *Being Fine: The Other F Word. Kapil@nibana.life*

Envisaging the Accelerated Future of the Crypto Economy

By Kapil Gupta and Rohit Talwar

How might the applications of blockchain technology and crypto assets lay the foundations for the crypto economy?

In this chapter we explore the range of crypto assets and applications that are emerging and the factors driving future adoption. The potential for further market volatility is discussed and an outline is provided of how the crypto economy might evolve in the coming years.

In the first of these two chapters we explained blockchain technology and crypto assets such as cryptocurrencies and crypto tokens, discussed key risks and concerns, and explored why interest in the sector is taking off. In this second chapter, we take a more detailed look at the types of crypto assets and applications that are emerging on the horizon. We also examine some of the factors impacting current and future adoption and look at potential domains through which the crypto economy could evolve. We close with a discussion of critical factors that could shape the near-term future of both blockchain technology and the crypto economy.

Types of Crypto Assets

To help our subsequent exploration of potential applications, let us start by examining some of the different current and emerging types of crypto asset. These form the base layer of the crypto economy, enabling the applications, and from which future possibilities could develop. Across all of these, progress is being made quite rapidly—particularly in regard to speeding up transactions and scaling the volume that can be handled.

Cryptocurrency–A digital monetary asset like Bitcoin (BTC) or Litecoin (LTC). These can be used to purchase goods, services, or other crypto assets. Currently, Bitcoin and the majority of cryptocurrencies are transparent; anyone can view the public addresses of user wallets and the transactions that have taken place in a crypto asset's network. This enables the "on chain" tracking and analysis of transactions, deposits, withdrawals, trends, and unusual patterns that might suggest attempts to manipulate markets.

Central Bank Digital Currencies (CBDCs) –Digital versions of fiat currencies such as China's Digital Yuan pilot project and the early stage plans for a digital US Dollar. The goal is to reduce transaction costs, simplify cross-border payments and money transfers, and improve social inclusion for the unbanked. Another key driver is to improve traceability of financial flows and reduce the potential for illegal financial activities such as shadow economy transactions, money laundering, fraud, and tax evasion. There are major privacy concerns here as, unlike with most crypto assets, CBDCs will likely require the identity to be known for the parties at both ends of a transaction.

City Coins–These are an emerging category of crypto based fund raising tools for municipalities. The first such example is MiamiCoin, a cryptocurrency powered by the Stacks Protocol, which enables smart contracts on Bitcoin. The goal is to boost the city's crypto treasury holdings while delivering crypto returns to the coin holders. The intention is that Miami will use the appreciation in these funds to support city investments in infrastructure, attracting inward investment, supporting startups, and creating tourist attracting city events.

Platforms–These platforms use a variety of different blockchain designs to create the core functionality used by others to build Decentralized Applications (Dapps). The first example of this was Ethereum (ETH), which is the second-largest cryptocurrency by market capitalization after Bitcoin. The vast majority of functional applications in the crypto arena run on the Ethereum platform which aims to be a "world computer" on which others can build Dapps and deploy smart contract functionality.

A range of other such platforms are emerging to compete with Ethereum—such as Cardano (ADA), Polkadot (DOT), and Solano (SOL). So-called Layer 2 platform applications such as Polygon (MATIC) are also emerging. These sit on top of Ethereum and effectively scale up the range and volume of activities that can be undertaken without overloading the Ethereum blockchain.

Stablecoins–These are typically asset-backed cryptocurrencies such as Tether (USDT) and USD Coin (USDC). These try to maintain the same value over time by tying themselves to a conventional asset like gold or the US Dollar. They are seen as an efficient means through which to trade other crypto assets without taking money out of the crypto ecosystem until a user wants to convert all or part of their holdings back into a fiat currency. Holders can often receive much higher rates of interest on their stablecoins via various Decentralized Finance (DeFi) applications than they would using fiat currencies via more traditional and centralized savings routes.

Utility Tokens–These tokens are usually issued by applications that run on top of a blockchain like Ethereum. An example would be VeChain (VET) which seeks to support all of the processes and information flows involved in supply chain management. Typically, a company initiates an initial offering where they sell utility tokens that can either be used as a form of investment in the company, or as a method of payment for services on that company's platform. As with other crypto assets, the tokens do not carry the same legal rights as investment in listed equities, and most are unregulated.

Social / Personal Tokens–Tokens typically issued and controlled by individuals such as celebrities and influencers (e.g. Katy Perry) to enable their followers and members to purchase a range of (often exclusive) branded goods and services. Such tokens might secure the owners' the rights to early and discounted purchase of event tickets, access to deals from brands and other celebrities, and participation in "token holder only" events with the celebrity in question.

Community Tokens–Tokens typically issued and controlled by a community, network, group, (e.g. $JAMM) and in some cases managed by a decentralized autonomous organization (DAO). Examples might include tokens issued by social media networks, sports clubs, and membership organizations, and associations, all of whom are look-ing to enhance the revenues while providing additional benefits to their communities. In the same way as some locations created local currencies such as the "Brixton Pound" for trading with local vendors, community tokens perform the same function. They could also enable community members to reward each other at the "going rate" for services such as dog walking, gardening, and house painting.

Corporate / Brand / Ecosystem Tokens–These would be issued by companies to enable their customers, followers, and wider ecosystem to buy goods and services from the brand and reward them with discounts, special offers, and additional tokens (e.g. Facebook Diem, Dance) as a form of loyalty points. The bigger the brand's network, the more valuable the community and token become, thus attracting other vendors to trade within the community. A key benefit here is that keeping transactions within a community using a specific token, the less need there is for third party credit card companies.

Security Tokens–These are a digital or "tokenized" form of traditional assets such as securities and options that already have a market value. They are effectively blockchain ledger-based contracts that secure the token holder's ownership stake in these assets. A key factor here is that the underlying assets are regulated by governing bodies that control how they can be issued, managed, and exchanged. Tokens are now being launched on exchanges such as Binance that allow users to buy tokenized versions of the shares in companies such as Apple, Coinbase, Microsoft, and Tesla.

Asset / Commodity Tokens–These tokens facilitate the trading of physical real-world assets, which are often commodities like oil or carbon, and that are typically regulated. They enable buyers to purchase small quantities of a commodity that normally come in larger unit sizes, e.g. a barrel of oil.

In the asset market, a house owner might choose to tokenize their property and then sell fractions of it to multiple buyers. The token holders could then receive rent from the occupiers of the property—issued as additional tokens. As the property value increases, so the price of the tokens should rise. Equally, a developer might tokenize an entire new housing project to fund its development. Once completed, buyers of individual units would purchase tokens in the marketplace and use these to acquire the asset. This would give the original token holders a fairly rapid return on their investment.

Key benefits of tokenization are the opening up of asset and commodity markets to small investors, total transparency, lower cost transactions, and faster settlement. Impact Tokens are a form of tokenization which are seen as a potential route to unlocking investments for projects with positive social and environmental impacts. Lowering transaction costs and opening up investment access to such projects could attract both individual and institutional investors and help accelerate their delivery and realization of the intended impacts.

Privacy Coins–In contrast to highly transparent coins like Bitcoin, privacy coins, such as Dash (DASH), Monero (XMR), and Zcash

(ZEC), are a category of cryptocurrencies which enable anonymous private blockchain transactions, obscuring both their origin and destination addresses. This might involve hiding a user's real wallet address and crypto balance and combining multiple transactions to prevent analysis of what happened on that blockchain. Many crypto exchanges have barred such coins and regulatory authorities are monitoring them because of the risks around tax evasion and money laundering.

Meme Coins–These are coins which generally have no specific utility but gain popularity quickly by spreading their message through social media. Those that succeed in becoming a meme are typically pumped by a user base keen to achieve stellar returns in a very short space of time. The most prominent example of these is Dogecoin (Doge), which was started as a joke but built a massive following and gained support from prominent influencers such as Elon Musk. At its peak in May 2021, Dogecoin achieved a market capitalization of over US$95 billion and a gain of over 300,000% on its launch price. A range of other meme coins have since risen to prominence such as SafeMoon (SAFEMOON) and Shiba Inu (SHIB).

Factors Driving the Next Waves of Crypto Adoption

Many see 2021 as the year of crypto explosion, with institutions such as MassMutual, hedge funds, and major corporations like Tesla announcing that they have added digital assets to their balance sheets. Global organizations like PayPal, Visa, and Square are now enabling crypto assets on their platforms. More recently, El Salvador became the first country to announce that it will accept Bitcoin as legal tender.

A Forbes article earlier in 2021 suggested that crypto is entering its fourth stage of adoption; having gone through exuberance, speculation, and utility, it is now beginning to achieve stage four—mass acceptance. On a daily basis there is a growing flow of news suggesting the sector is expanding: announcements are made of advances in blockchain technology; founders explain how their crypto applications are adding more functionality; corporations herald their partnerships with different crypto platforms; influencer podcasts discuss features being launched on crypto exchanges; companies like Walmart, Amazon, and Apple announce that they are building digital currency teams; and reports highlight increasing interest from national governments, financial regulators, and the wider corporate community.

On an almost weekly basis we hear of financial institutions creating crypto investment vehicles, exchange traded funds, client advisory services, crypto trading platforms, and custody offerings. We are also seeing growing levels of interest and activity around direct investment in a range of cryptos by wealthy individual investors such as Mark Cuban, sovereign wealth funds, institutional investors, and other financial institutions. What these developments suggest is that, irrespective of short-term price movements, there is clearly growing belief in the long-term potential of the sector.

Crypto Market Volatility–Risk and Potential

Despite growing levels of interest and participation across society, crypto markets remain highly volatile. The massive price fluctuations will continue to both deter and attract potential market participants. Over the period since the launch of Bitcoin as the first cryptocurrency in 2009, the market has experienced numerous dips and crashes, but with an overall upward trend in value.

Total market capitalization for all cryptocurrencies rose from US$192 billion on January 1st, 2020, to US$776 billion on January 1st, 2021, and almost US$2.5 trillion by the middle of May 2021. After the crypto market crash that followed, the market capitalization fell significantly to around US$1.3 trillion with a 40% to 80% downward correction in prices across the crypto ecosystem. The majority of analysts and commentators in the market were suggesting that, if previous cycles were an indicator, this was a consolidation period before a major bull run.

Volatility extends into the mid- to long-term future. Various pundits have offered a wide range of predictions for the future size of the crypto market, which usually follows the direction set by Bitcoin. Depending on which side of the line you stand, i.e. for or against crypto, the

Bitcoin market capitalization predictions range from zero to US$10 trillion—matching or even overtaking that of gold.

Many analysts and crypto proponents are arguing that this is the new Internet and that the likes of Bitcoin, Ethereum, Cardano, Solana, XRP, and Polkadot could become the future technology titans, usurping the current leaders such as Apple, Amazon, Microsoft, Alphabet (Google), Facebook, Tencent, Tesla, and Alibaba.

Rise of the Crypto Economy

Those actively involved in developing these fields, and exploring their possible future, envisage them evolving to provide the basis for a radical rethinking of how financial markets and economies operate. They suggest we are seeing the very first steps in the journey to a truly democratized and transparent crypto economy, one where every citizen has the opportunity to participate fully and enhance their financial fortunes.

The evolution process has been rapid. In 2014, Ethereum emerged as a new type of blockchain. In addition to providing a store of value like Bitcoin, this provided a platform with the capability to run smart contracts and thus enable a range of applications where decentralization was a desired outcome. For example, Decentralized Finance (DeFi) has become one of the key areas of growth in the use of blockchain technology. The aim of DeFi is to democratize the financial markets by making functions like lending and borrowing available to everyone with very low transaction fees and high rates of return, and all without the need for centralized entities like banks.

A wide range of blockchains are emerging, supporting an ever-growing array of applications which are driving the rapid expansion of the crypto economy. Some early stage examples and upcoming use cases of blockchain technology and crypto assets would include:

Decentralized Finance (DeFi)–Blockchain technology has enabled the establishment of an ever-growing number of decentralized "Automated Market Makers" such as PancakeSwap (CAKE) and Uniswap (UNI). These providers enable the exchange of tokens and offer access to decentralized crypto-based versions of products ranging from savings and loans through to more complex instruments that are available in traditional markets—such as liquidity pools and derivatives. The goal is to put activities such as saving, lending, borrowing, and the full range of more complex financial products, in reach of everyone, irrespective of their wealth and income.

Decentralized Autonomous Organizations (DAOs)–Organizations where the entity exists entirely in software, has no employees, and governance is done by the community. A number of such examples exist in the DeFi space described above, and in sectors such as insurance where firms like Teambrella are pioneering the disruption of more traditional markets. Some suggest DAOs could be a totally transparent and highly participative model for the future of business, government services, and even of democracy itself.

Blockchain Enabled Decentralized Supply Chains–Applications range from monitoring the flow and provenance of goods from producer to market, through to the funding of agricultural smallholders. For example, VeChain (VET) is a blockchain that is working with companies changing how farmers can get access to funds by validating their produce on the network without relying on third parties verifying them.

Non-Fungible Tokens (NFTs)–The creation of a range of uniquely identified digital assets ranging from an educational qualification certificate or the deeds to a property through to limited edition digital collectibles such as artworks, music, and sports memorabilia. This development has the potential to revolutionize the creative space by giving greater financial power and returns to the artists. Marketplaces are being established where artists can monetize limited editions of their work. This could include all the stages of development on route to the final product, e.g. the artist's sketches behind a painting and early studio versions of songs before the final version is released.

NFT technology enables the artist to create a specific digital identifier token for their work, thereby preserving the uniqueness and rarity. The NFT concept is spreading rapidly with organizations looking at applications as diverse as event ticketing, digitization of collectibles such as sports cards, and even limited edition "digital only" apparel.

Content Distribution Using Blockchain—Decentralized social media platforms that enable users to own and monetize their own content such as videos. Imagine the possibilities that could emerge from owning all of your content on YouTube, Twitter, Facebook, TikTok, and other social platforms—as opposed to handing it over to these centralized companies to monetize. For example, LBRY.com is a content sharing and publishing platform that is decentralized and owned by its users. Another example is AIOZ.network, a blockchain-based content delivery network that hosts AIOZ.tube, a decentralized competitor to YouTube, where the content is fully owned by its users.

Decentralized Artificial Intelligence (AI)—Platforms that enable end users to select and integrate modules to build their own AI applications. An example of this is SingularityNET (AGI)—a project that is creating a decentralized library of AI algorithms and tools.

New Payment Methods—Business models that allow customers to pay using crypto assets and then gainshare with the vendor should the value of the crypto asset appreciate when compared to the original purchase price in the underlying fiat currency. While an increasing range of commercial entities have started to accept payment in Bitcoin and other cryptocurrencies, take-up by end users has been low. This is because the potential for future capital appreciation of the crypto asset far exceeds the price of the goods and services on offer. However, a number of businesses have started looking at the idea of crypto payment with gainsharing. For example, imagine paying for the next five years of holidays with a single up front crypto payment and then sharing the future gains on that asset with the travel provider. This secures the cost of future holidays for the consumer, while locking in their business for the travel provider.

These are just a few examples of the ever-growing range of use cases that blockchain technology facilitates today and could enable in the near future.

Conclusion–Enabling the New Economy

The ideas presented here only scratch the surface of what might be possible in a post-pandemic future. Both blockchain and crypto assets can be seen as potentially revolutionary developments that aim to redistribute power and financial freedom from centralized control to the wider population. Hence, the philosophy behind the technology is seen by many as anti-establishment and has drawn a lot of criticism especially from centralized authorities, particularly when it comes to regulation. As such, there is still significant resistance and risk aversion among many in more conservative and late adopter governments and traditional centralized industries.

For some time to come, the public is likely to be put off by the complex nature of the underlying concepts and technology. Equally, concerns will remain over its relative infancy, high volatility, and the perceived risks of crypto assets, all acting as further barriers to mass adoption. For this highly technology-centric sector to achieve the goal of mass adoption it will have to work hard to address these concerns and learn from the best of the current consumer-facing technology providers.

Equally, there is also a growing groundswell across society of those who are attracted by the potential financial liberation offered by crypto assets. There are also many in business and national governments who are becoming more engaged and excited about the possibilities of blockchain as an advancement of the Internet. There are clear benefits of moving from a centralized model to a more automated, lower cost, decentralized approach to a wide range of activities.

Like any technologies in their early stages of development and growth, both blockchain and crypto assets have their obvious risks. So, while some may consider the landscape outlined here to be the unregulated Wild West of the Internet, others see the potential and are working to put in place appropriate safety nets. It seems likely that, in the coming years, we will see the start of a regulatory framework around crypto assets that seeks to bring elements of centralized controls and regulation to an unfettered and unregulated decentralized phenomenon.

Risks and concerns notwithstanding, the next five years are likely to see a massive expansion of learning, engagement, and adoption of blockchain and crypto assets across society.

- *In an increasingly complex world where centralized systems are coming under growing pressure, what alternatives could there be to blockchain-based decentralized solutions?*
- *What opportunities and challenges could the shift to a more decentralized and self-governing operating model create for individuals, society, businesses, and governments?*
- *Where might we still require centralized systems to act as arbitrators and managers in an increasingly decentralized world?*

Kapil Gupta is a technology and crypto analyst, commentator, enthusiast, and investor. He is a transformational coach to business executives and entrepreneurs and the founder of Nibana.life. Kapil is a TEDx speaker with an MBA from the University of Edinburgh Business School and an undergraduate degree in Computer Systems from the Open University of British Columbia. He is a co-author of *Being Fine: The Other F Word. Kapil@nibana.life*

Rohit Talwar is a global futurist and the CEO of Fast Future, where he focuses on the future of financial services and the crypto economy.

Post-Traumatic Growth: How Might Business Change for the Better?

By Richard Freeman

Could the pandemic be the catalyst for businesses to embrace bigger picture thinking and smarter localized decision-making?

The Economy is Dead. Long Live the Economy?

This chapter sets out an optimistic scenario of how businesses might transform over the coming years in response to the pandemic and broader societal aims around sustainability in all its dimensions. The focus is on the British context, but many of the ideas discussed have broader global applicability in a world where we are looking for workable and innovative solutions to the economic challenges laid bare and amplified by the pandemic.

In this scenario, British business seizes the opportunity to think big and evolve into a series of new social economies, driven by sustainability and inclusive growth. As a result, the post-pandemic era looks positively rose-tinted as individuals, businesses, and governments recognize just how deep the integration is between our pillars of innovation, health, education, and cultural identity.

In making this journey to a brighter future, major lessons can be learned from the recent past. During the fallout of the global financial crisis, entrepreneurs were discouraged from taking risks. Trust in systems, institutions, and public services was eradicated. Regional strategy was replaced with what turned out to be weird, fractured, and mixed-quality marketplaces in key pillars of society such as education, adult social care, and the arts. People stopped talking to each other, in favor of protecting their IP and assets at all costs. The fallout from the pandemic might be much, much worse. But I don't think it will be.

The past decade was a steep learning curve for British society. A recession, Brexit, a more acute North-South divide, political stagnation, and a climate emergency have all, I believe, been both a cause and a result of weak decision-making and an erosion of civic confidence and community collaboration. In my optimist's scenario, we thrive, because of three things: thinking big, contextualized decision-making, and the fluidity of skills.

Thinking Big

Unlike in the austerity years, I believe that, in time, people will think big again. Don't get me wrong, we're in for a bumpy ride with the UK's Office for Budget Responsibility expecting a £300 billion (US$386 billion) bill to repay, but I believe the energy for change will be different.

The pandemic showed how fragile many sectors are, from just-in-time logistics to technology startups now categorized as "unviable" because they aren't yet profitable. Business culture has been upended. In 2017, the Centre for Economic Performance in the UK identified the English new town most able to weather and benefit from a hard Brexit as Crawley in the south-east, because of its proximity to, and resulting growth from, Gatwick, London's second airport. However, the 2020 UK Centre for Cities' pandemic resilience report found Crawley would now be the worst affected English town on every measure, with over 50% of jobs at risk.

As we look to the future, maybe Crawley will be fine. Strong public–private problem-solving and focused local networks are demonstrating a cross-sector response and opening up ideas, with investment in local innovation, and £12 million (US$15.7 million) released by the local authority in grants to businesses very quickly. Co-design between state and enterprise solves problems where the free market alone often fails. This doesn't have to be the case just in emergencies.

We could mitigate against collapse through strategic design and making decisions at a cross-sector and regional level. Executive business boards have often tried to hide behind brick walls of protectionism and simply try to elbow their way back to growth. While such behaviors may have been cheered across society in the past, they could now become the poster boys for greedy opportunism in the new world. Instead, we saw big engineering firms creating value by inviting in clinical expertise to create sanitizer, ventilators, and personal protective equipment (PPE). These initiatives and partnerships to deliver innovative short-term solutions could lead to valuable and transformative long-term relationships.

In this scenario, the mantra isn't survival of the fittest, but survival of the most useful. The hope is that a younger generation of business leader sees this moment as a reset; becoming more conscious of their place on the UK "You Are Here" map. Post-traumatic growth is about our relation to everyone else—not how far we leave everyone else behind. We are what impact we have on our customers. We are what we are connected to.

A good example of what might be possible is 3DCrowd, a DIY network of around 8,000 micro-manufacturers who came together in a matter of days and collaborated to produce face shields for frontline health workers treating infected patients. Working at scale to an agreed design blueprint, the network produced over 500,000 face shields on 3D printers—buying raw materials in bulk and centralizing distribution logistics in real time. It was not perfect, but it was radical, big, and very, very fast.

Purpose is not just possible, it is necessary. And big thinking is incredibly infectious. Over the next 12 months the gig economy, and the self-employed, are very likely to pool their resources and become more unionized, centered around networks that flex, acting bigger than the sum of their parts, driven by radical collaboration.

Context is Everything

The goal of radical collaboration between technology providers and communities has been tinkered with for some time, but we could now see a rapid escalation of what data-driven innovation really looks like.

The balance between central control and localism is a tightrope of nuance, resources, and data security. But technology innovators are making it possible for communities to better determine what products and services they need—from emergency transport to fresh beer delivered from the local pub or brewery. Cornwall has not had the same pandemic as Manchester—so while still part of a collective effort, its local recovery needs different tools.

Design-thinking principles are common in business as a technique for rapid user-centric innovation. In the public sector Adur and Worthing Borough Councils in Sussex, England have been rethinking services using the approach for a few years now. During the pandemic they have accelerated the sharing of aggregated intelligence to aid food distribution, galvanize volunteers, and check in on the vulnerable. They have embraced real-time testing and learning and collaboration with private delivery companies and community organizers using an app, challenging the cliché that local government is generally slow and risk averse.

Over the next two years, some of the possibilities tested during this pandemic will not easily be put back in a box. Unusual collaborations could become more visible, with a greater element of shared risk. Traditional political barriers will be harder to justify, and more public money could flow to underwrite innovation.

Fluid Skills

One of the biggest barriers to business growth in the UK, has been the frustrating pigeonholing of skills. Creating diverse workplaces has been a hard slog; it is much easier to mirror the existing team when recruiting than to bring in people with different skills, mindsets, and experience. In my utopian vision, things are very different. The very notion of skilled and unskilled gets redefined as the country embraces skill *sets* rather than job roles. Theater set designers helped build a hospital in nine days, pediatric surgeons retrained to be intensive care unit (ICU) nurses, and gin distillers shifted production to make clinical-grade hand sanitizer.

In a post-pandemic world, the hope is that we realize that it is *who* we are, not *what* we are, that helps us to be productive. The reality is that problem-solvers, makers, carers, and organizers exist in every organization and shouldn't only be used in a crisis. A generation of children have just missed out on their exams, but instead may have better understood the value of negotiation, communication, resilience, and creativity regardless of job title.

This pandemic can open up a new skills conversation, focused on transferability, flexibility, and diversity, versus simply recruiting people because they can put tab A into slot B.

I might not get everything I wish for, but as the dust settles, hopefully this disruption will have given us permission to do things better.

- *What support do governments need to provide to enable radical collaboration in every sector?*
- *Can greater sharing of knowledge and data between the public and private sector lead to faster and more flexible decision-making?*
- *Could businesses grow faster if they focus more on the skill sets they need rather than the jobs that have to be done?*

Richard Freeman is CEO of always possible. He is a specialist in organizational strategy, work-based learning, facilitation, inclusive growth, and cross-sector innovation.

Business Leadership Skills—Navigating a New Landscape

By Steve Wells

What are the critical skills required to help organizations navigate a path to the future?

There's so much I could discuss here about what it will take to help organizations navigate a post-pandemic future. However, in this chapter, I am going to focus on three areas that resonate particularly strongly for me: integrating foresight with change, coaching in a post-pandemic world, and embedding foresight to create a route to the future. Let's start with foresight and change.

Integrating Foresight with Change Methodology

As our world has changed, we've tended to continue using more traditional change models focused on systems, processes, structures, and business models. Arguably, the people side of change can be an afterthought, only noticed as missing when things don't work as planned.

However, the pandemic challenges organizations to consider an uncertain future and the implications for people in the change process. Organizations seek ways to resurrect themselves, ensure post-pandemic success, and do so with an energized, informed, and motivated workforce. Yes, we must deal with what's in front of us now, but in parallel we also need to look at what lies ahead.

Change is about people, individuals, their unique needs and motivations, and their different experiences and skills. Perhaps the pandemic will prove to be the tipping point for a far more human-centric perspective on organizational change, paying attention to the cultural and behavioral norms at the heart of transformative change.

What are some of the lessons we should take and apply to future change programs? The first is to appreciate how we as people naturally respond to change, how it causes unease and uncertainty, which in turn can set up resistance to the change we are trying to implement. A sense of uncertainty, about the future for example, generates a strong threat or alert response in our limbic system. Our brain detects something is wrong, and our ability to focus on other issues diminishes.

We don't like uncertainty; it feels like a type of pain and is to be avoided. Certainty on the other hand feels rewarding, and we tend to steer toward it, even when it might be better for us to remain uncertain. When the very first thing we want to do is develop trust in the organization then good, clear, concise, and honest communication is crucial, even about uncertainty.

There's another factor here. Are we building a change program that fixes a problem we are experiencing in the present or have experienced in the past? Or are we invested in developing change that is fit for the future? Building flexibility, agility, and resilience into change programs by exploring plausible scenarios is crucial for the future growth of our enterprises and the wellbeing of employees.

Using foresight, we can establish a future-fit change vision and build resilience and agility into change plans that might otherwise have been inflexible. We can do this by integrating foresight into a human-centric change methodology; by exploring trends, by horizon scanning for developments, ideas, and wild cards, and through the use of scenarios.

Coaching in a Post-Pandemic World

The pandemic has had a disruptive impact on working patterns for many people. Key challenges have included coping with working from home, isolation from the workplace, missing out on the benefits of being in a work centered community, and the inability to draw on serendipitous collaborative working opportunities. Although change happens all the time, during the pandemic period it's been more profound, happened much faster, and created an increased sense of anxiety. In part our response has been to turn to technology. Healthy or not, in the UK, Internet use more than doubled in 2020 due to the pandemic as just one example of this.[10]

This period has provided leadership challenges, with increased team conflict, more stress, and greater anxiety, for example. Coaching is a potential tool to support adaptability, acceptance, development of a flexible mindset, and reinstate a proactive rather than reactive outlook.

Despite this super-charging event to our already VUCA (volatile, uncertain, complex, ambiguous) world, the foundations of coaching remain the same and demand for it is growing both among experienced leaders in mature businesses and those in startups.[11] The basic drivers remain unchanged; looking for solutions to work-related challenges, personal transformation, achieving a specific career goal, and feeling supported through a period of extreme complexity and uncertainty. Coaching can help to access our natural resilience and enhance our feelings of wellbeing. It can enhance our natural sense of connection with other people that might have been lost through multiple lockdowns and remote working.

As we look to the future, coaching must address a challenging agenda critical to both mental wellbeing and corporate success. Requirements include finding solutions to help cope with the increasing pace of change and embracing our reality. This in turn means exploring uncertainty and adapting our cycles of learning and practice. This all requires help to build awareness of what is changing around us, and in making sense of the present and possible futures.

Coaching can be the crucial tool in helping us make the transition from surviving to thriving. There's a major challenge here for coaches in the current reality. We have seen rapid growth in the use of platforms such as Zoom and MS Teams that open up the opportunity to coach the client from anywhere in the world. However, coaches are in the business of coaching because they value working with people in person. For many clients, the best outcomes have been the result of good coaches in face-to-face interactions; in such situations it's better for the client and better for the coach.

Nevertheless, we can expect increasing deployment of technology in this most human-centric of personal development interventions. An example might be increasing use of apps to support meditation and aspects of coaching practice. This could perhaps even extend to the use of artificial intelligence (AI) as part of a diagnosis process.

Technology offers digital alternatives to multisensory live coaching. Some live sessions could be delivered virtually, making use of comprehensive data analysis covering factors such as microfacial expressions and body language. The experience could be extended further through use of avatars and virtual and augmented reality to create simulated interactions. While this may seem undesirable now, our collective ease in interacting with machines may play a significant role in driving acceptance of these interventions in the future.

Integrating human coaching practice with digital platforms seems almost inevitable. Building on the notion of collective intelligence, perhaps the use of technology will support experiential, felt, and connected client experiences rather than replacing the coach. After all, can a machine be interested and curious at the human level?

Embedding Foresight to Create a Route to the Future

Let's start by considering mindset. We have a binary choice about how we consider our place in the emerging future, a simple stick or twist option. We can play by the rules of the game we are used to playing, doing what we have always done, to get what we have always got. However, as the world moves on, we risk becoming irrelevant. Or we can play by new rules, play a new game, and explore new opportunities. It was Einstein who said, "Insanity is doing the same thing over and over and expecting different results."

Kodak and Blockbuster are two perfect examples of what happens if you stick and don't twist. We all know the consequences of Kodak's infamous decision to bury their invention of the digital camera, and

Blockbuster missing the potential of the Internet and turning down a partnership offer from a young Netflix. A broader look at the age of corporations is also revealing. An often touted statistic attributed to McKinsey reports that the average life span of companies listed in Standard & Poor's 500 was 61 years in 1958. Today, it's less than 18 years. McKinsey also predict that 75% of the companies currently quoted on the S&P 500 will have disappeared by 2027. This poses the question; how do we stay relevant?

A shift in mindset takes us to leadership, and into what I frame as a period that requires extraordinary change leadership. In the past we have been confident about how the future might play out, and able to reach consensus about how to proceed. This is the realm of ordinary leadership dealing with relatively tame problems. Increasingly, we are much less certain about the future, and far less able to reach consensus about the way ahead. This is the realm of extraordinary leadership in the face of wicked problems.

This distinction suggests that, to take our organizations forward into an increasingly turbulent future, leaders need to facilitate development of organizational culture that builds a willingness and capability to imagine and experiment our way to the future. This is enabled by encouraging and nurturing accelerated learning, entrepreneurship, systems thinking, creative thinking, tolerance of uncertainty, contextual sense making, foresight, and scenario thinking.

Pre-pandemic, there was evidence of increasing interest in foresight. The disruption brought about by the pandemic added a sense of urgency. The challenge for futurists is to find the sweet spot inside the entity where there is both the ability to embrace and adopt a future-fit mindset and a willingness to challenge and change the organizational DNA. Typically, we need to find stakeholders who are open to different perspectives and ideas, who are collaborative, and who genuinely seek engagement across the organization.

Connection to the enterprise's current reality can be crucial, as well as integrating foresight with key organizational priorities and processes such as strategic planning and organizational change programs. In an ideal world, we might also see foresight linked to leadership development programs to help build organizational capability.

So how might our foresight work be enabled and enhanced by technology? A great start point is the notion of Collective Intelligence—defined by NESTA as "something that is created when people work together, often with the help of technology, to mobilize a wider range of information, ideas, and insights to address a challenge." This provides the ability to support collaborative and continuous foresight by combining human sense-making skills with the power of automated data collection, aggregation, and initial categorization.

But what about future potential system developments that might further automate foresight work? The likely increasing sophistication of intelligent systems with more automation in the connection of trends and drivers might create insights in their own right, independent of humans. Perhaps the combination of augmented and virtual reality will enable us to "physically" manipulate and experiment with the data in 3D to create new and previously unconsidered insights and therefore create new possibilities and foresight outputs. Perhaps, automated foresight platforms and systems will one day create our scenarios for us and update the insights and implications in real time.

In the meantime, while smart tools can help us more and more, as the ultimate sense-makers, humans will continue to make informed choices that respond to and shape the emerging future. Hence, in my view, a grounding in foresight should be a critical leadership skill.

- *What foresight mechanisms does your organization use and how supported are they at each level of leadership and management?*
- *How does your organization approach the integration of foresight with core activities such as strategy development, operational management, and the delivery of key change initiatives?*
- *How are post-pandemic organizational coaching models being adapted in the face of future challenges and opportunities?*

Steve Wells is an experienced futurist, facilitator, and founder of Informing Choices Ltd, specializing in futures and foresight.

Changing the Way We Work

By Steve Wells

How can we reframe organizational thinking away from change management toward change readiness to help prepare us for an uncertain future?

There have been many lines written about how work will change in the future and how that process has been accelerated by the pandemic. But here, I want to address the implications of continuous change on work and how the changes might impact the way that we work in the future.

The Implications of Continuous Change on Work

So how do continuous change and ambiguity shape how we plan for the future of work? Critically, we might need to change our mindset in a number of ways. Our organizations can become stuck in cycles of "execute at all costs." However, if we genuinely believe that change is more than simply a constant, and that its pace and scale are increasing, then we need to shift toward a more agile, flexible, and adaptive mindset. That's not to say we stop planning, but that we do so in the knowledge that we will have to change our plans. This is surely lesson number one from the pandemic.

There's a fascinating conflict in many organizations. While the world has always been uncertain, the volume of data and information we have today makes us feel more comfortable about handling uncertainty.

We expect to be able to resolve problems instantly. Some changes and trends we can map and track but, even with foresight, it doesn't mean we can foresee everything. So competence in how we deal with change and uncertainty is key.

We should also pay attention to the human implications of continuous change. Put simply, it is exhausting and yet likely to be our reality for some time to come. So what are the implications for how we work and stay in work?

Acknowledging that continuous change is everywhere and requires a different way of thinking is a start. In our workplaces, change increases anxiety and challenges how we make sense of the world. Being constantly confronted by change and challenge is mentally draining, so organizations need to recalibrate how we work and rest to optimize performance.

This is a question of leadership. Leaders need to understand the physical and mental implications of change and dial the insights into how they lead their teams and organizations. In part, this starts with understanding the implications of their own words and actions on people around them. Effective leaders in the 2020s and beyond need to consider how his or her communication style, actions, and ability to respond to uncertainty helps to create an optimal environment to allow people to excel in an ever-changing work world.

Of course, our world has been on a journey that was always going to change the world of work. Work is likely to become more dynamic and shapeshifting, more focused on outcomes. But in seeking to also alleviate stress and the mental health implications of continuous change, leaders will have to find ways of "humanizing" work and identify human-centric models that support change and build productivity. It seems like a no-brainer, but at the heart of this is to look after and value the workforce first, so they can look after your customers and clients.

Changing the Way We Work

As the world maneuvers its way through the pandemic, collective attention will turn toward a post-pandemic period. If they have not done so already, all types of organizations across the commercial, public, and third sectors will have to consider their proficiency in dealing with future disruptive events and develop greater resilience.

Given the speed at which things have changed—and continue to change—there is no quick fix in making such a paradigm shift. Organizations should explore the implications on how we work in the future, what the drivers of future change might be, and develop resilience to change and disruption.

Foresight can help us explore different possible futures. Within this context, organizations will continue to consider evolving working models around home, remote, and distance working. This means adopting an operational model that is more empowering of the workforce and more human-centric. A model that requires less command and control and enables change agility through a distributed structure, with decentralized decision-making supported by rapidly evolving digital tools.

Whether remote working becomes the norm rather than the exception in the post-pandemic future remains to be seen. There have been underlying trends in this direction, which the pandemic has accelerated. Many people will point to the benefits of reduced commuting, a sense of safety from minimizing the number of times one has to mix with potentially infected strangers, and a better life–work balance.

On the other hand, others have been predicting a bounceback to office working because of perceptions about productivity, the social benefits of working together in the same physical space, or simply the preferences of an organization's executive leadership. One other trend to dial in here is the growth of contract or contingent workers who might work remotely as part of distributed, autonomous teams. The question that arises here is what might become of corporate culture in companies composed mostly of remote or hybrid working teams?

Culture happens when we are together, socializing as people, so will culture survive such a shift in working practices? What does a future decentralized organizational culture look like? What are the new behaviors, skills, and creative thinking required to develop and maintain a culture that includes hybrid and decentralized working?

Technologies such as artificial intelligence (AI), increasingly efficient collaborative working platforms including video meeting applications like Zoom, become necessary technologies to enable a more decentralized working model. But how far might businesses be willing to push the use of these new working models?

The balance between remote and on-site workers and the balance between automation and people will change the underlying DNA of an organization, and it will change the expectations of the workforce. How much of what an organization will choose to do in the future will be driven by competition for talent, regulation, taxation, and further disruptive events? What are the implications for leading the inevitable change programs now? Perhaps the answer lies in the idea that we don't focus on managing change, but instead we focus on change readiness.

- *What does your organization see as the critical success factors in preparing for an uncertain future?*
- *What actions are being taken to enable change readiness at all levels across the organization?*
- *What are the critical lessons to take from the pandemic about how we lead into the future and develop leadership talent?*

Steve Wells is an experienced futurist, facilitator, and founder of Informing Choices Ltd, an insights business specializing in futures and foresight.

The Future of Retirement in the Post-Pandemic Era

By Michael Nuschke

How might the pandemic impact our strategies and choices in plan-
ning for retirement?

The starting premise for this chapter is the assumption that, over time, the pandemic will be controlled successfully by a combination of developments including an effective global vaccination roll out, booster shots, treatment protocols, and gradual herd immunity. A supporting assumption is that there will be a multi-year, staggered economic recovery. Within that scenario, the chapter explores the potential impacts of the pandemic on retirement planning.

Retirement is an economic and lifestyle goal for a large percentage of people in developed countries. Increasingly it is also on the radar for the growing segments of middle classes and wealthy citizens in many developing nations. For some, this is a matter of attaining financial independence where working to earn more money becomes optional. Or it may be the traditional winding down of a career and end of work based on age and pension eligibility.

Retirement planning has recently been shaped by expectations of living longer and needing to fund a longer retirement. There has been a rise in "staged retirement" through reducing the number of days or hours worked, and continuing to work part-time after retirement. The December 2019 19th Annual Transamerica Retirement Survey found that 55% of Americans believe they will need to work past 65, mostly due to not having enough money to retire.[12]

A widespread retirement savings shortfall suggests many people, if not most, are not well enough prepared. Almost half of US households aged 55 and older have nothing saved for retirement.[13] Many of the rest have only relatively small amounts saved. The impact of the recent pandemic will only make these shortfalls worsen. Similar patterns were starting to appear in other developed nations pre-pandemic.

Sudden changes brought on by the pandemic could help drive the adoption of a new kind of thinking about retirement. This is something I believe needed to happen anyway, since, for many people, it will be a situation of running out of money before running out of life.

What then are the possible influences on, and resulting choices we might make for, the post-pandemic future of retirement? To help us understand the possibilities, let's focus on three key areas of impact on retirement planning: financial, lifestyle, and health.

Financial Implications

Globally, investment markets took a severe hit when the pandemic's potential impact became clearer and, despite market recoveries, many economies have contracted. Overall market uncertainty has increased, making retirement sustainability more uncertain. Huge increases in national debt in many countries creates more uncertainty in outlook and could significantly impact overall economic growth, currency valuations, and potential future inflation.[14]

The clear risk is that pension plans will become less sustainable. The ability to pay the expected pension commitments could be undermined by a combination of low interest rates, stock market declines, and lower employee contributions due to spikes in unemployment.

Uncertain incomes typically result in less spending and more saving. This is especially so for retirees who no longer earn employment or business income. Now, overall increases to discretionary expenses may occur due to pent-up demand, but for retirees, more careful spending patterns could occur for years to come. The importance of having an emergency fund was brought home by the pandemic. Going forward, those that can save will likely want to build up their own emergency fund, and this again could result in less spending.

An increasing number of retirees, or those approaching retirement, will likely look to create other businesses or part-time income in response to greater income uncertainty. The transition to an online business might be made easier by the recent growth in personal use of online video conferencing for calls with family, and the experience of ordering goods for delivery using online commerce. This could be a significant opportunity for those who had long thought that a digital business was not for them.

Many countries have also responded with direct-to-citizen financial benefits. This might lead to more acceptance of the need for Universal Basic Income programs in the future, which would also help reduce uncertainties around retirement income.

Lifestyle Implications

In the face of pandemic uncertainty and the risk of viral spread of virus variants, many may think twice about discretionary travel far from home for some time to come. Certainly, we are likely to be more interested and conscious of the local medical systems wherever we travel to. While finding an ideal retirement destination may have been in many people's plans, the pandemic may make it a higher risk proposition to move abroad to a country with an underdeveloped or less accessible medical care system.

The housing choices of those in or approaching retirement may also be altered. Some may opt to live with their extended family, but for others this simply isn't an option. For those living alone, with months of experience of social isolation, the benefits of living in a more spacious home with yard space could become a more important preference. Digital solutions to social isolation may also increase. Growth in use of digital assistants, home care robots, and video conferencing to stay in touch with family and friends, are just a few examples of the different forms of digital company that are emerging.

The hesitation by many older people to buy things online has likely been overcome due to necessity during the pandemic. Retirees new to online commerce are often victims of online crime—particularly savings theft. They will need to be vigilant to avoid the many online scammers, and an increasing array of protection solutions may emerge.

Continual adult education is a key strategy for those entering or in retirement. Going forward, this is likely to be more digital than physical. Online learning for its own sake, and learning how to earn an online income, are likely to become even bigger trends going forward.

Health Implications

Use of Telemedicine services has surged during the pandemic. Once used, the acceptance of virtual medical care is likely to spread—like a virus. Notably, in the US, Medicare now covers telehealth visits. Many healthcare systems around the world have seen the efficiency and quality of care benefits of moving to online consultation for the majority of patient interactions. Most are likely to retain this model long after the pandemic has been conquered. Part of the savings made may also be passed to the customer in systems where the patient pays through insurance or at the point of access.

Key to avoiding future viral outbreaks could be increased funding for companies promising to boost the immune systems and overall health of older people. The severity of pandemic cases and the mortality rates increase with age and preexisting conditions. Many researchers point to weakened immune systems as a contributing factor in higher infection rates for older people and those with secondary conditions.

Some biotech companies[15] targeting immune system health say these treatments might improve viral resistance. As a result of an increased focus on optimizing health, some people living longer and healthier may be a surprising outcome of the pandemic.

Accelerating progress of regenerative medicine like stem cell therapies may also have significant impact on life expectancy. This would have major potential impacts in terms of extending working lives, and in the amount of money required to lead a happy and healthy extended retirement. In this and other areas, the current prolonged discover-to-therapy timeline could be speeded up through freeing up of more funding, use of artificial intelligence, and a faster regulatory approval process. The economic and social costs of this pandemic, and the outsized impact on older people, make increased funding, research, and progress a greater imperative and more likely.

More generally, those who have, or can develop, stronger immune systems and remain in overall better health, can experience reduced personal risk in viral pandemics. This enables those same people to become and remain active and productive. They will likely spend significantly less on healthcare expenses and may choose to take on or continue some form of employment or business activity.

Retirement—The Next Chapter, Not an Ending

The pandemic accelerated changes in many areas impacting today's version of retirement. While the financial implications are largely negative, these rapid changes could trigger new perspectives on what retirement means. Most importantly, a renewed focus on health may accelerate the slowing and eventual reversal of aging. When effective health extension and rejuvenation therapies, retirement could become a next chapter versus an ending.

- *How would a prolonged economic depression further impact sustainable retirement?*
- *Post-pandemic, will people really change their behavior and perspective or revert to previous ways?*
- *How will the notion of retirement change if rejuvenation therapies succeed in radically extending healthy life spans?*

Michael Nuschke is a retirement futurist, writer, and speaker. After a 30+ year career as a retirement planner, he realized that a retirement planner was really a "closet futurist."

THE GLOBAL OPERATING ENVIRONMENT

Post-Pandemic Geopolitics: Three Scenarios

By Max Stucki

How might the pandemic accelerate and influence future geopolitical developments?

Even though the outbreak is far from over, its impacts on the geopolitical landscape are already discernible. One of the key change drivers is that the pandemic has deepened existing distrust between some nations. The thus-far dominant wave of globalization and international crisis collaboration is challenged by closed borders, calls to repatriate production, and the desire to prioritize each country's own needs.

To help map out and explore the possible geopolitical situation out to 2025, three scenarios are presented of how the major economic powers have fared over that period: China—A Recovered Dragon, The United States—An Isolated Giant, and Europe—A Dream Shattered. Although highly speculative, the thinking is based both on the classical geopolitical tradition, and the present situation.

China–A Recovered Dragon

The Great Pandemic struck China first. Chinese officials, once forced into action, were quick to contain the viral wave originating from Wuhan. Strict—and sometimes harsh—measures ensured the majority of the population was safe, and that the economy could restart reasonably quickly. While other nations struggled and went into recession, the pandemic appeared to accelerate China's rise.

Rapid reaction and assistance rendered to other countries ensured a growing prestige and influence. Having dispatched medical staff all over the world, China was able to cultivate relationships and gain a foothold in states that were previously not among its closest friends. China's manufacturing strength enabled it to mobilize a supply chain in response to a rapid rise in global demand for personal protective equipment (PPE). China's ascendancy was further aided by the stumbling of the US in handling the situation. China capitalized on the former hyperpower's moment of weakness and projected a picture of decisive leadership and strength.

Now, in 2025, China is the largest economy in the world on all measures, including nominal GDP. Thanks to the acceleration provided by the pandemic, it has been able to tie a number of countries in Eurasia closer to itself through both trade and aid. A 1904 article by the English geopolitical theorist Halford John Mackinder, argued that "whoever rules the 'World-Island' (comprising the interlinked continents of Europe, Asia, and Africa) commands the world." His nightmare had been realized, thanks to a small virus that at a crucial moment created the opportunity to unite the supercontinent under the leadership of Beijing. Although suffering from the loss of some of the manufacturing plants transferred back to the West, domestic demand is now keeping the Chinese economy afloat.

The United States—An Isolated Giant

Although the US was the leader in all things medical at the beginning of the 2020s, the pandemic still spread rapidly across the country. Despite massive financial actions by the government, the economy recovered slower than anticipated. Furthermore, a devastating blow was dealt to the dollar's value in early 2023 through a deal struck by large oil-producing nations to start selling oil priced in China's renminbi. Facing a real possibility of hyperinflation, the Americans could no longer engage in quantitative easing to keep themselves going.

Many working for the public sector witnessed pay cuts and layoffs. The armed forces also got their budgets slashed, albeit their pension schemes remained almost intact. This meant fewer ships, fewer planes, and fewer soldiers to fight America's wars. The economy of the US was able to finally pick up speed, partly thanks to production lines repatriated from China; an action that inflamed relations between the two. Despite the recovery, there is a feeling that the days of American supremacy are over. The petrodollar is mostly dead, and despite being the second-largest economy, the US is now a country among countries, even if a significantly strong one.

Europe–A Dream Shattered

The European Union (EU) was hit hard by the pandemic. The knee-jerk reaction of most member states to close borders showed that, in times of dire national emergency, domestic needs were prioritized over the shared interests of the Union. Past talks about the necessity of abolishing borders and the need for greater unity vanished. In practice, it turned out that the EU was not able to act as a coherent entity to fully combat the pandemic. For some time, it was every country for themselves. Despite a common EU-wide recovery program, economic growth remained weak at best and in some places was virtually non-existent. The entitlement programs started to erode and even collapse in some places as the debts accrued during the pandemic forced austerity on everyone.

Member states also stopped taking asylum seekers and migrants, as there was hardly enough work for even their domestic populations. By 2025, the EU's common currency, the Euro, which created shared financial responsibilities, had been abandoned by the largest members to avoid backing each other's debts, driving further devastation.

China's presence in Eastern Europe became more and more visible. Eastern countries fared better after the crisis as Beijing favored their exports as a way of dividing the Europeans. Russia, despite having suffered from the pandemic, resolved the situation in Ukraine to its advantage in late 2022, while the US and EU were still focusing on internal matters of post-pandemic recovery.

Europe in 2025 is starkly different from Europe in 2020. The economy is stagnant, lavish government handouts are history, and populations are shrinking due to low birth rates and drastically reduced immigration. Democracy is at risk in some places, as emergency pandemic control measures remain in place. Europe waits for the next storm knowing it will stand alone. The capitals of the Old Continent listen carefully to Beijing's statements, which is now their most important economic partner. The EU still exists, but more as a symbol of the past, as hardly anyone heeds its feeble commands.

Concluding Thoughts

The world will almost certainly change due to the pandemic, which seems to be accelerating global developments that might have played out anyhow. The scenarios explore how these could lead to China's rise, weakening of the US, and growing distrust between EU states. Naturally, things could go quite differently. Perhaps the US emerges victorious from the pandemic, having developed not just a vaccine, but also a cure that truly eradicates the virus. Perhaps China's strength and decisiveness at the start of the pandemic are deceptive, and its claims mostly propaganda. Perhaps Europe is united not divided by the challenge. Many questions remain to be answered.

- *What is the lasting geopolitical legacy of the pandemic?*
- *Could the pandemic change the direction of geopolitical trends altogether or only accelerate them?*
- *What part will the pandemic play in the potential end of the geopolitical supremacy of North America?*

Max Stucki currently works as foresight analysis manager at Futures Platform, a company focusing on strategic foresight. He has a special interest in creating and analyzing geopolitical scenarios.

A World Transformed: Political and Socio-Economic Impacts of the Pandemic

By Dr. Doaa Alghalban

How might the economic and political fallout from the pandemic impact international relations and society over the next five years?

A New World Order Takes Shape

The pandemic has been a huge global tragedy, threatened many human lives, raised new fears, and reoriented relationships due to social distancing. The pandemic has also handed governments powers they would never normally acquire, due to an unprecedented need for interventions. It has shown the fragility of our existing systems and triggered the start of a radical remake of our world.

Many political analysts, global thinkers, and futurists believe that global systems will not remain the same after the pandemic. Key indicators such as world conflicts, weaknesses in financial systems, and growing inequalities were already pointing to the inefficiency of current governance systems, which have now been made even more apparent by the crisis. This chapter examines the issues emerging during the response and recovery stages of the pandemic and provides some insights into how all these factors might come together to shape the possible future over the next five years.

Shifting Economic Power

Global geopolitical uncertainty is a critical future influencing factor here, with strong possibilities of a new global system emerging and power moving eastwards. This possibility is supported by faster economic recovery resulting from a generally better response to, and control of, the virus by nations such as Singapore, South Korea, and even China. Secondary and tertiary waves of infections have tested their resilience.

Many of the more developed Western nations have suffered deep economic declines. This may in part be because they took longer than their Eastern counterparts to respond to the crisis, acknowledge the need for extensive control steps, and announce lockdowns. As a result, the European nations of Italy, Spain, France, and the UK have suffered heavy casualties, while the US seems to have been in the eye of the storm with the highest number of infections and deaths of any country at the time of writing.

The question now is whether, in the longer term, national populations will have more or less trust in their respective governments over the handling of the crisis and, for some, the state of public services. Consequently, governments could react in different ways, for example by exercising more control and thereby undermining freedom. Alternatively, they could become more transparent and open with their citizens and governance processes. The choices made here are likely to determine the direction countries take, both in handling domestic political agendas and in framing their foreign policies and international relations.

A lack of trust internationally could adversely impact America's leadership in the world, particularly given the growing influence of Eastern powers such as China. The latter could be seen by potential economic and political partners as smarter, increasingly confident, and more resilient if they succeed in winning the pandemic battle sooner and with less relative damage.

A faster post-pandemic recovery could see eastern markets like China and Singapore experience continued growth in the next two to five years, albeit potentially at a slower pace than before due to adverse global economic conditions. The situation is far more uncertain for other developing markets globally, like India, Indonesia, Brazil, and Mexico. Prior to the pandemic, the expectation was that growth would be driven by their knowledge workers and a young and growing population. However, high and rising pandemic-related infection rates and deaths could well set back the pace of development for many, with a long and slow process of economic recovery.

There is the clear potential for China to be in a position to replace the US as the main sponsor of the post-pandemic globalized economy. Several factors are driving this. South China Morning Post reports that, since 2013, China has invested around US$690 billion in the development of the Belt and Road Initiative—a program touching up to 160 countries—and with an estimated US$4 trillion of projects already underway prior to the pandemic.[16] In addition, alongside its reputation of being the world's factory due to its extensive manufacturing capacity, it has committed a reported US$430 billion to developing global leadership in artificial intelligence (AI) as the next critical global industry.

China and the Next America

A significant drop in the value of the dollar could also create the need for a new united global currency that derives its power from the global economy. With an eastward power shift, these countries may benefit from more favorable currency exchange rates, accelerating their rise in the world order.

So, when these factors are combined, although the US has extensive experience in how to lead, support, and make global alliances, it is China which may gain more political and economic influence, allowing it to emerge as the foremost global superpower. For China to assume a bigger role in the global order, this could mean helping to rebuild countries in need, taking urgent steps to control emissions and the impact of climate change, and building stronger and broader global trade partnerships. These actions might help reduce the intensity of

US policy actions toward China and help it gain greater respect on the world stage.

Economic Impacts on Nations and Society

Globally, increasing levels of debt, due in part to the cost of surviving and recovering from the pandemic, will likely impact the economic sovereignty of several national governments. This could increase the potential for greater political control by the donor nations and institutions that help finance any bailouts and support measures. Poor countries could increasingly be forced to seek financial assistance, resources, and expertise at a time when many world powers are also struggling to recover and rebuild their domestic economies. In such circumstances, President Biden will need to work hard to restore America's global political influence and reverse President Trump's increasingly nationalist focus.

We could see more international economic and political conflict due to a rise in countries adopting a nationalist response and focusing their financial resources internally to ensure domestic recovery and self-sufficiency. For example, the European Union (EU), hit hard by the pandemic, might gravitate toward disintegration. This could mean poorer EU nations may depend less on the US and search for more effective and supportive partners. This would create opportunities for China to gain both economic and political influence to help further its interests. The question is, what would countries have to offer up in return for that support?

Economically, the pandemic has already had a huge impact on unemployment rates, with estimates of tens of millions of jobs lost globally and women and the low paid often being the hardest hit. At the same time, we are seeing major GDP contractions in previously growing economies, and there are increasing warnings of a deeper and longer world recession than in the global financial crisis of 2007–08. With expectations of continued economic volatility globally, for many, disposable household income will likely continue to decline and translate into adverse socio-economic effects. These could be more pronounced for the most vulnerable sections of society, particularly the elderly, the differently abled, women, children, and the poor.

The pandemic and subsequent social distancing and lockdowns are expected to have long-term social impacts, such as aggravating psychological problems for people struggling to cope with the unpredictable world changes and the consequences of unemployment. Rising death rates are already making some people value relationships more and realize the necessity of physical interaction alongside virtual life.

To combat unemployment and a depressed and demotivated populace, governments are expected to invest more to develop skills in sectors such as healthcare, education, and technologies such as artificial intelligence. Many nations are also expected to increase the level of social welfare benefits and create different policies to secure the rights of essential workers. However, it will be the much-needed focus on mental health and coping mechanisms—especially for children, women, and the vulnerable—which will have the greatest impact in determining how we emerge from this crisis.

To reiterate, this crisis has challenged, and potentially changed, the existing global systemic framework of institutions, alliances, policies, and relationships. It has raised critical questions about the status quo in economics, politics, diplomacy, healthcare, and crisis management. Adopting a positive way forward requires nations to come together in newly formulated partnerships, rather than pursuing the current trend toward narrow nationalist perspectives.

Without building enduring partnerships to tackle issues emerging from the pandemic, it will prove difficult to find solutions for such complex challenges. As we look to the future, it seems nearly impossible for any country to flourish alone in the information economy, with its intricate and highly interconnected web of physical supply chains, and complex global flows of money, data, and knowledge.

Today's political governance models, ranging from democratic to highly autocratic systems, have evolved over time. These have built on historic power structures that derived from religion, economic power, physical might, feudal systems, and hereditary dictatorships. This pandemic has the potential to shift us toward a new version of power.

For much of the last 70 years, America has exported its democratic principles, economic models, and social values, establishing them as important pillars of a recipient country's success and assimilation into the global order.

Now, the world order is on the verge of unprecedented change. The Eastern powers are preparing to assume positions of greater authority and influence, but potentially with less societal freedom. Whatever governance model is adopted, in a world of constant change, we can expect people to value physical, social, and caring relationships more than virtual interactions.

- *What might the distribution of global power and influence look like five years from now?*
- *How might the eastward shift of economic power impact the decision-making and behavior of global corporations?*
- *What are the possible implications for citizens around the world of China assuming greater economic and political influence?*

Dr. Doaa Alghalban is a strategic advisor on foresight strategies, governance, public policy, quality, and excellence management for different government organizations in the United Arab Emirates (UAE). She currently works as senior consultant at Alghalban Professional Consultancy Services in Norway. Doaa holds a Doctorate in Business Administration with a focus on public policy development and implementation.

National Security in the New Normal

By Brett Peppler

How might the pandemic experience shape national security planning in the new normal?

Framing Security Policy

Could what began as a public health issue, with deepening economic impacts, also pose enduring national security concerns? This chapter uses scenario analysis to explore what national security decision makers may learn from the pandemic, and how this might shape national security in the new normal over the next two to five years.

At the core of national security planning are two key concerns for decision makers: articulation of national interests, and the exercise of national power in pursuit of those interests. The pandemic demonstrated that the ability to deal effectively with transnational issues is constrained where interests and the exercise of power are too narrowly defined. Both President Xi's pretensions to a new China-centric international order and President Trump's "America First" doctrine could be seen by some as representing narrow interests and a discordant approach to international engagement. Some would argue that these policy approaches obfuscated, delayed, and dislocated the responses of both China and the US to the pandemic.

Assumptions About the New Normal

In order to frame the scenarios, some underlying assumptions need to be clarified. Firstly, it became clear that from the start of the pandemic in 2020, the world would be different in many ways and that some of the near-term consequences of these changes were likely to influence national security planning, especially the nature of national security. However, having an intellectual understanding of the new normal will not be the same as internalizing its reality.

Public health expenditure and surveillance are likely to feature more prominently in national security plans as many governments refocus their longer-term budgeting and start to treat pandemic preparedness with the same priority and urgency as traditional security threats, such as terrorism. Furthermore, dependence on global supply chains for critical goods, and the extent of national stockpiles of these supplies, could occupy an increasingly important role in the strategic calculus for many nations. Finally, many countries will have difficulty recovering from the crisis, with economic weakness, fragile health systems, and total state failure likely to become ever more prevalent features of the post-pandemic world.

Security Scenarios in the New Normal

The axes and poles of the scenario space are *the articulation of national interests* (from narrow to broad), and *the exercise of national power in international engagement* (from "power over" to "power with"). These are suggested by Joseph Nye's body of work on strategy and power. The four resulting scenarios are presented below.

Scenario One—Toxic Nationalism

National interests are narrowly defined, and national power is exercised over others.

This scenario is not unlike the initial responses to the pandemic, where countries focused on their own security and wellbeing. Over the period to 2025, great-power competition between the US, China, and Russia becomes the primary determinant of geopolitical concerns. This competition will likely contribute to the ongoing deterioration of Sino-American relations, with both sides using the pandemic to improve their own position in the competition. Locally, there is a turning inward, reinforcement of the movement toward nationalism, and a vain search for autonomy and self-control.

Without the incentive to protect the earlier shared gains from economic integration, global economic governance weakens. It will take enormous self-discipline for political leaders to sustain international cooperation. International institutions starved of resources may fail. The most dangerous outcome would be for national security decision makers to surrender to forgetfulness and hubris. This scenario signals movement toward toxic politics in a meaner, poorer, and less secure world.

Scenario Two–Pragmatic Nationalism

National interests are narrowly defined, and national power is exercised with others.

In this scenario, narrowly defined national interests remain pre-eminent but national power is leveraged among foreign partners in a transactional sense for short-term gains. These transactions may not be solely for altruistic purposes, as leaders seek to buy domestic political capital while shifting the blame for poor security outcomes to partners. In the aftermath of the pandemic, the perceived need to dedicate resources to rebuild at home means there is a reduced willingness or commitment to tackle regional or global problems, including climate change. Indeed, the economic consequences of the pandemic reinforce nationalist sentiment and global disengagement.

Scenario Three–Shared Insecurity

National interests are broadly defined, and national power is exercised with others.

In this scenario, the new normal heralds the grim reality that no nation—however strong—can protect its security acting alone. A shared sense of insecurity introduces the greatest potential for collective action, and the rejection of great-power competition. Empowering others—often through the nuanced use of soft power—helps nations accomplish their own goals. Extensive scientific collaboration in the race to develop a vaccine featured a coordinated multinational research and production effort which has spilled over into broader collaboration across a range of global challenges. The new normal features greater commonality and harmonization of reporting systems, controls, and contingency plans—which must be pursued as a means of mitigating mutual risks. Over the longer term, this scenario may lead to a more pragmatic internationalism.

Scenario Four–Enlightened Self-Interest

National interests are broadly defined, and national power is exercised over others.

Short of widespread collective action, this scenario imagines the expansion of existing coalitions under leadership inspired by enlightened self-interest. International cooperation is directed toward mitigating the risk of dislocation of developing nations and others with large numbers of economically vulnerable workers. There is an opportunity for international society to reperceive norms, behaviors, and platforms for coordination and collaboration. This scenario signals movement toward a world where economic globalization takes a back seat to environmental globalization, as represented by pandemics and climate change. However, advocacy for a broader global agenda jeopardizes the support of citizens still embracing a populist view.

Uncertainties

The global reorientation of national security strategies and reordering of threat priorities were triggered by previous international security challenges, such as the Cuban missile crisis and the 9/11 attacks. The key question now is how powerful the pandemic experience will be in reshaping national security planning, especially in terms of challenging its underlying assumptions, paradigms, and governing systems. Every nation puts its interests first, so a shared sense of insecurity could cut both ways; either intensifying existing geopolitical conflicts or crystallizing collective action.

However, we have not yet witnessed a reorientation of national security due to the pandemic, which lacks the shock of a deliberate and imminent threat from a hostile actor. Resistance to change will be exacerbated by the political context, especially authoritarian leadership, and ideologically-based agendas. Short of strategic reorientation, most states are likely to improve their national security architecture and decision-making processes around pandemic threats to mitigate the effects of poor planning, missed signals, delays, and incoherent policy responses.

- *Will a "new normal" help us deal appropriately with the pandemic's wider implications—beyond health and economics?*
- *Will the pandemic experience reshape national security planning, especially in terms of challenging underlying assumptions, paradigms, and governing systems?*
- *How will a new shared sense of insecurity shape future national security priorities when every nation puts its own interests first?*

Brett Peppler is managing director of Intelligent Futures Pty Ltd. He specializes in the creative application of strategic foresight to frame and navigate complex business challenges.

Three Possible Futures— Choose Your Preferred Story

By Joana Lenkova

How might the decision taken today impact the scenarios that could play out over the next 20 years?

In times of crisis, such as the one we are currently living through, our ingrained responses are to fight to preserve and restore our lives to their pre-pandemic status. However, it is now, more than ever, important for us to recognize and appreciate the opportunity we have to reconsider our priorities, review our existing societal systems and lifestyles, and rebuild our future in new and better ways.

In this chapter we take a journey into the future through three plausible different worlds and the choices they present.

A Brand-New World is prosperous and sustainable, there is global collaboration, and people live in harmony with nature and technology. Corporates are more sustainable and work in the best interest of all stakeholders.

My Own Personal World is one where technology facilitates progress, and our lives are more convenient but at a cost. It's a world of failed governments, where companies own all our personal data.

A Hot New World is a scenario where we build higher walls and divide our world, instead of collaborating. The effects of the pandemic are long-lasting across all areas of our lives and the health of our planet is neglected.

These scenarios unfold as a result of colliding economic, scientific, social, technological, and environmental developments and the decisions we, as society, must urgently take today. Let's explore the three future worlds and the choices that drive them.

A Brand-New World

You wake up and it's pleasantly chilly, just as you like it, thanks to Sol, your home artificial intelligence (AI). Sol monitors your biometrics and sleep behaviors, and automatically adjusts temperature and moisture to create the most pleasant home environment. The blinds go up, the coffee is already brewing, smells of freshly baked croissants fill the air, and on the living room wall you see projected a scene depicting a spring day in Paris. Sol is trying to give you an endorphin boost. You appreciate the effort as you had a late night at the National Health Research Centre. Your health tech company has big news to announce to the public today—a universal respiratory virus vaccine!

The pandemic unlocked investment for research and innovation in healthcare, leading to a massive breakthrough that could save millions of lives. It took years of research and global collaboration between governments, universities, and the private sector to get here, but it was worth it. The vaccine eliminates the need for seasonal reimmunization and protects us from different strains of respiratory viruses.

Following the 2020–21 pandemic, companies focused on sustainability and the adoption of the Economics of Mutuality management model, benefiting not only shareholders but all stakeholders: people, planet, and company. At the beginning, it seemed like a utopian concept, but the pandemic proved it to be a sustainable way to do business, enabling companies to live longer and be more profitable. Choosing long-term sustainability over short-term profit was the right decision to make.

Looking back, there was a gradual societal epiphany during the pandemic leading to a value shift. People now dedicate more time to family, altruism, and education. A Personal Social Standing (PSS) score was introduced, measuring everyone's contribution to the world's global sustainable development goals, and rewarding them with access to certain services, entertainment perks, and upgrades to their AI devices.

My Own Personal World

The baby is still sleeping. SecondSkin, the digital patch on your wrist, reminds you it is time to prepare her food as her vitals are showing she will be awake soon. You had the option to bioengineer her DNA as it is now common practice for parents to exercise their recently legalized right to remove genes associated with hereditary disease. Choosing a child's physical attributes is also possible, if not yet completely legal. There is an ongoing ethical and regulatory debate over whether we should leverage scientific innovations in body and brain engineering and augmentation to fully design a baby's eye color, intelligence, or physical strength.

Gene editing unlocked a wave of experimentation and exploration in the field and is now among the top paid occupations. Research in this area gave us additional benefits—aging has slowed down and our pets live twice as long.

The package with the baby's supplements has arrived, pre-curated for her new developmental phase and includes food ingredients, vitamins, clothes, and toys. A subscription service drone delivers all of these items for the entire family right to your door. You get points added to your overall PSS score for exercising regularly and eating your personalized diet, created in accordance with your DNA profile. Preventive care is a huge part of the healthcare system.

As the most fragile governments crumbled in the wake of the pandemic, so large companies stepped in. Googlezon now owns the data for your city, as well as its telemedicine platform. You have some rights, of course. You can choose how much you share, but your PSS score is impacted by it. You like to get hyper-personalized services and products, whenever and wherever you need them. However, you some-times feel trapped in the bubble. If you are feeling more adventurous, you try to confuse the algorithms by making random product choices, just because you want to try something new.

A Hot New World

It's been a tough few years since the pandemic. The researchers are still struggling to find a broad based and universally affordable vaccine or cure that covers the widest possible range of constantly mutating variants. Climate change and shifting weather patterns brought new diseases and stricter control on movement and social contact was needed. Borders were closed and we started living more secluded digital lives. We now long for personal contact but are limited to immediate family and a handful of geo-proximate friends. International travel is almost impossible, so we take virtual vacations. Our main concerns are now cybercriminals and identity theft.

In hindsight, we deployed too many resources searching for and rolling out a solution to the pandemic health threat, which hit some economies hard. Global trade seized up in favor of higher cost local and home production of essentials. Those limited by space or ability are relying on government rationed powdered food, which is fortified with essential vitamins and minerals.

With borders closed, rising sea levels and severe drought created new threats and illegal migration, which in turn brought unrest and conflict. The plans for floating cities were never realized due to lack of funding and short-termism. When there are fires to put out, there is little time to experiment and dream of a better future.

Refugee camps and poverty are a common sight these days. However, we did also make some good decisions during the pandemic. Governmental incentives were given to companies and individuals that produce renewable energy. Air pollution was dramatically reduced but global warming continued, and we are now adapting to the impacts by building houses with less glass and thicker walls. It's still hot. Very hot.

Conclusion

Any of these scenarios is plausible and which parts of them become reality depends on what decisions we, as society, take now. We could build *A Brand-New World* if we prioritize research investment, sustainable practices, and global collaboration. Alternatively, we could create *My Own Personal World*, where convenience is key and we advance scientifically and technologically, but our governments fail to protect our privacy and freedom. Perhaps the biggest risk is that *A Hot New World* could evolve as a place where poverty, disease, nationalism, and the creeping effects of climate change are taking their toll, because nations failed to recognize the urgency and acted alone rather than in collaboration against a global threat.

Will we take the opportunity to build a future in which we are better equipped to face the challenges of the new world? Or will we try to hold on to the past, resisting the change?

- *What are the driving forces and trends arising today that could have the greatest impact on tomorrow and the next 20 years?*
- *What does the future you want to live in look like and what choices would you need to make to get there?*
- *What will happen if you choose to take no action in the face of the changes taking place in your life and in the world around you?*

Joana Lenkova is a strategist, futurist, and founder of Futures Forward. She helps organizations build resilient strategies for the future. In 2021, Joana joined the LEGO Group's Creative Play Lab as a strategic foresight director. The opinions and ideas presented here are her own.

The Day After the Lockdown

By Alejandro Repetto

Which of the changes that we are experiencing today could define the future?

The system has been reset. People are shocked by the present. The media keeps on pushing numbers and statistics about the spread: infections, death rates, vaccinations, and recovery. Most governments are at a complete loss as to how to balance the pandemic's impact on the health system with its impact on the economy. Companies are struggling to survive, rethinking their processes and business models, facing fast-forced digital transformation. This situation repeats daily, as if we were caught in the time loop from the movie *Groundhog Day*.

The big question is "Who is thinking about the day after the lockdown?" This in turn raises questions about which things might change forever after the disruption of the pandemic. How can we make smarter decisions today so we can be better prepared for tomorrow? Using foresight methodologies, this article proposes plausible, challenging future scenarios full of risks and opportunities to help make better decisions today.

We are receiving many signals of change; an avalanche of indicators that do not fit with any particular pattern or trend line. By using the approach of future design, organizations can gain a better understanding of the possible futures that could emerge and hopefully use them to guide more sustainable actions in the present. Which of these signals will become critical drivers of change in the next two to five years? This scenario had been developed by selecting the following set of signals:

1. Working from home (WFH) emerging as the only way to keep operations up and running in a lockdown and the option of choice for many once restrictions have been lifted.
2. Digitalization of businesses that before the lockdowns were mostly physical.
3. The cultural and societal impacts of social distancing and online social meeting (from birthday parties to friends' barbecues).
4. An accelerated pace and scale of bankruptcy among small to medium sized businesses ravaged by the loss of revenues during lockdowns.

Using these signals, a timeline to the future can be created: the near future of the next 12 months after the pandemic is considered to have been conquered in any particular country; the mid-term future of between one and two years after the lifting of the lockdowns; and the long-term future looking between two and five years after the lockdowns are lifted.

The Near Future

In the near future, the world seems set on a course of increasing instability. Unemployment is predicted to continue rising due to waves of closure of an unprecedented number of small and medium enterprises and growing redundancies among larger firms around the world. Governments and their social services systems may experience a continued and perhaps unprecedented growth in demand. Organizations that are still viable might maintain WFH as a transitionary measure of social distancing.

Businesses related to the support of online operations may continue to be among the biggest winners of the crisis. Online meeting platforms, cloud computing, virtual private network services, system security professionals, and online marketplaces will continue to be essential for companies that survive the crisis. The crisis has also brought to light the processes and actions that can be digitized and the ones that must remain physical. This boundary is changing all the time, for example in areas of medical assistance and aspects of the justice system.

The Mid-Term Future

Over the next couple of years, the world could reach a new steady state. Traditional organizations will increasingly be able to measure the impact of WFH on their cost base and performance. The data will also provide a better understanding of whether investing in big office infrastructures is the best option going forward. Many internal processes will inevitably change in order to support employees alternating between working on and offline, depending on the tasks they carry out.

Digital transformation initiatives might be given a boost during and after the crisis and new ways of working could arise. Improved digital literacy levels and changing market dynamics could help managements develop a clearer understanding of where to invest for maximum impact. Companies that were forced to migrate part of their business to digital service delivery may keep both channels open. Customers would then be free to engage both online and physically, depending on what they find more convenient. Organizations might become more "phygital"—both physical and digital at the same time. The training course provided by the pandemic could help many companies become more flexible and resilient to deeper and more frequent situations of volatility, uncertainty, complexity, and ambiguity.

The world might see a rise of entrepreneurs not necessarily related to technology. Many of the newly jobless, in the developing world in particular, might choose to start small low-investment businesses such as micro-convenience stores, cooking home-made food such as pastries, or engaging in any number of businesses that do not require a high level of technical knowledge.

The notion of phygitalization could cause many aspects of societal infrastructure to be reshaped. Around the world, there may be a need to invest in Internet infrastructure in order to support a potential doubling, or more, in the amount of data traffic—driven by an increase in WFH employees. In some countries, the Internet may be declared as a basic societal service, on the same level as clean water, gas, or electricity. Also, because of digitalization, fewer people are likely to be commuting to and from their jobs, reducing traffic jams and rush hour crowds on public transport.

The Long-Term Future

Stepping forward to five years after the pandemic has ended, life could be different in many ways. Some of the new entrepreneurs might succeed and grow their businesses into major players. Shifting patterns of trade brought about by the pandemic, coupled with technologies such as blockchain, mean the economy could be more decentralized, functioning in a meshed ecosystem. This transformation could increase the stability and resilience of the economic system.

Phygitalization may have a direct impact on people's quality of life. Reduced commuting could lead to a permanent decrease in the carbon footprint of the ecosystem and increase the amount of spare time available to people. The migration to online working might have a considerable direct effect on family structures and dynamics. Houses could be reshaped to support WFH, including suitably equipped working spaces.

Office buildings might be repurposed to residential use. Due to widespread adoption of online marketplaces, there could be even more idle commercial premises. Real estate pricing could be depressed, and cities might be reshaped. Less transport infrastructure would be needed. Fewer cars and buses and smaller streets could give place to expanding public areas.

This scenario might help decision makers to take a more sustainable view of the future. Responses during a crisis should be executed at two levels:

1. Mitigation, with short-term tactical actions aiming to reduce the immediate impact of the crisis.
2. Transformation, through mid- and long-term actions to be ready for a range of possible new realities.

Future design is a tool that helps leaders plan and execute transformational actions, thus increasing the chances of survival of their organizations.

- *How can we ensure that decision makers factor in the possible future implications when they take short-term actions?*
- *How prepared is your organization to survive in a phygital world?*
- *How robust is your organization's vision of the future and how is it being used to shape sustainable strategies?*

Alejandro Repetto is a foresight and innovation strategy practitioner and serial maker. Passionate about the positive impact of technology on the world, he creates and implements solutions today to change the world tomorrow. He has co-funded and leads advanced technology companies that help organizations to make a positive impact in the world.

REGIONAL AND NATIONAL FUTURES

Reimagining the World Order to Regenerate African, Caribbean, and Pacific Economies

By Dr. Claire A. Nelson

How can nations in Africa, the Caribbean, and the Pacific recover and regenerate their economies?

September 20th, 2027: The following speech by the architect of the SMART Futures Paradigm was aired live worldwide on the interactive multimedia Africa World Channel, from the United Nations General Assembly in New York. Billions of people worldwide eagerly awaited the United Nations' announcement on the SMART Futures Fund's multi-pronged approach to decision-making and rapid-response resilience engineering under Sustainable Development Goal (SDG) 17—*Partnerships for the Goals*. The regenerative economics model proposed by the Ubuntu Economy Agenda is the pillar around which a robust, resilient global economy is being rebuilt from the ruins left by the economic devastation set off in 2020 by the pandemic crisis.

"Welcome to ACAPA Rising—the African Caribbean Pacific Alliance (ACAPA) Civil Society Forum—the third since our founding in

2022 and the official launch of the Ubuntu Economy Agenda. We have arrived here after a harrowing journey through the wilderness of what many of us call 'The Holy Transition' and we have good news. The good news is that we have created our Forum as a parallel but integral part of institutions that in the past excluded us.

"Today, ACAPA countries enjoy a telehealth network that penetrates 30% of all the primary cities and secondary towns in the ACAPA countries. With the funding we have received from Diaspora Health Bonds, matched by our friends in the philanthropy sector, we are reaching 10 million people with our mix and match solutions such as Lab2Go Xpress, Pharmacy-in-a-Box, and Clinic-in-a-Car Solutions. Our goal is presence in every ACAPA country by 2030. Our ongoing challenges of access to information and communications technologies (ICTs) and energy are being addressed through relationships we have built with global technology and engineering organizations.

"In terms of education, 30 universities in ACAPA countries have partnered with universities in the 'Global North and South' to form the Consortium of Sustainable Future Centers. We count among our successes the establishment of Blue Economy Decision Support Systems Centers and the launching of the ECOWASAT 12 array CubeSat in 2024, a satellite built through the collaboration of ten universities in the consortium.

"The good news also includes the online training and certification system for healthcare professionals which has been able to graduate over 10,000 healthcare workers in ACAPA countries. The skills certificates awarded cover various allied health roles such as radiology and lab technicians, nursing assistants, health tech app managers, and telehealth chat room assistants.

"This ragged band of 150 ACAPA outcasts, outlaws, outliers, heretics, and troublemakers have seen our vision of multiplying circles of 150 take root and spread, and we are now 15,000 strong and growing. We began this journey neck-deep in dread but holding onto hope, knowing that for us, children of the formerly enslaved, our ancestors have survived much more horrific events.

"In the arc of change making, there is what the social scientists call the 'inciting action.' For most of us in the ACAPA diaspora, the fact that blacks in America were dying at a higher rate from the pandemic than other segments of the population, and the news that the then US president had denied the export of ventilators to Barbados and test kits to Jamaica were the tipping point. The ensuing anger and terror became the energy that fueled our action. The Healthy Futures 2030 Online Summit that was convened in summer 2020 became not just a US event but a global one addressing our organizing question: 'How can the ACAPA diaspora work with agents on the ground to test and scale responses to the pandemic, while at the same time advancing the goals and targets of the SDGs?' What resulted was the articulation of the Ubuntu Economy Agenda.

"Ubuntu, which brings our shared vision of recovery and regeneration into reality, focuses on health, education, and economy. We understood that a regenerative economy demands sustainable systems, meaningful metrics, adaptable and agile agency of all actors, robust resilience of the systems, and transformative use of technology. Our agenda was predicated on the recognition that we are interdependent, and our economy should create a 'safe and just space for humanity.'

"We borrowed heavily from the lessons of the anti-apartheid, civil rights, and Garvey movements in order to spread the 'SMART Future Gospel' as a space in which everyone could be a change-maker. We all knew that we could not go back to the old paradigm of 'capitalism gone cancerous.' The pandemic gave us a common pursuit: 'How can leaders of heterogeneous societies create abundant opportunities for all in the absence of a unifying agenda?'

"Was it easy? No! The fear was great. We had seen Michael Manley and Winnie Mandela castrated. We had seen Lumumba, Malcolm X, and Martin Luther King assassinated. So black leaders who think about structural change understand that you make the move at some risk. But we made the choice.

"As we look toward 2030, there is a lingering fear of pandemics, and of course there is still climate change. In the past, leaders in the progressive movement have used Martin Luther King, Jr.'s quote, 'The arc of the moral universe is long, but it bends toward justice,' as if to suggest that there is an inevitability that justice would prevail.

"We understood that the justice we believed in was not preordained, and that we had a choice. It was to make music together and play a symphony of hope or to struggle as disparate members of a Greek Chorus with limited opportunities for survival. We felt in our bones that given the power structures in place, the moral universe would not bend unless we awakened to 'everyone a change-maker' and 'each one, teach one' actions to help to bend the arc of justice to save us from 'The Matrix' we feared.

"We made the right choice to act, even though we had no idea of how exactly we would address the known knowns, the known unknowns, and unknown unknowns we faced. Today, we come together as the engineers of this movement we have co-created and architects of the vision we are still building. Together we are seeding change and bearing witness to the future we want to birth. Together we are bearing hope."

- *Is it plausible to believe that we can create a scenario with an active, engaged, and empowered civil society across the globe, and where are the signals of this occurring?*
- *Is it realistic to imagine that we might see the rise of a movement that is at once local and global, and which enables alignments across Global North and South with deep technology transfer?*
- *Can this moment of reset provide the necessary and sufficient conditions for a truly global movement in support of the transition to a regenerative economy?*

Dr. Claire A. Nelson is lead futurist at The Futures Forum. A sustainability engineer, she is a proven social innovator and founder of the leading Caribbean American advocacy organization, the Institute of Caribbean Studies.

Futures of a Post-Pandemic Africa

By Leopold P. Mureithi

What scenarios could emerge for the future of Africa in a post-pandemic world?

Even as the world remains in the grip of a pandemic, one could wonder: what might the future of a typical African country look like when the crisis is finally over? This chapter will explore the developmental choices likely to face a typical African country. The preexisting conditions for many countries in Africa can be summarized through six archetypical ESPECT domain characteristics:

- *Economic status*—third world, donor and debt dependent.
- *Social structure*—trust deficit, limited social security, appalling health services, elitist education systems.
- *Political situation*—uneasy, dysfunctional, weak governments.
- *Environmental conditions*—challenged, fragile.
- *Cultural outlook*—diverse, complex, in some cases paralogical.
- *Technological capacity* – largely lagging behind most other countries, with pockets of innovation.

These six ESPECT domains highlight some of the glaring and fundamental systemic risks and opportunities that could shape the prospective outcomes for societies across much of Africa.

When the pandemic spread to Africa, many of its countries instituted emergency knee-jerk containment responses to counter the threat to human life. We witnessed lockdowns of whole countries or parts thereof, night curfews, closure of learning institutions, banning of public gatherings, and a range of social distancing measures. With such actions, most normal social activities were scaled down or suspended altogether, with net adverse consequences.

Despite the development, mass production, growing global distribution, and administration of vaccines, for many parts of Africa it could take until well into 2023 before the bulk of the population have had their first full set of vaccinations. After that, the pandemic is likely to have a lingering but manageable global footprint, much like many other diseases. This would become part of the new normal. So, in exploring the 2022–2025 time frame—and while much of this future is unknowable—in this chapter I anticipate some of the options by presenting a menu of choices among many possible futures. This requires us to explore and embrace the most critical uncertainties in place and a fleshing out of possible future scenarios.

Uncertainties Galore

Many African nations could experience serious negative long-term impacts from the pandemic and its economic effects, not least because lockdowns constrain the supply and availability of critical goods and services. The underlying uncertainty is the resilience of the production capacity of many African countries.

One of the critical internal uncertainties is how long many African governments will continue with enhanced emergency control mechanisms they adopted, and how deep they will be. A big external uncertainty is how quickly the global economy will recover and provide inputs, export markets, aid donor support, and investment finance. These uncertainties have the capacity to trigger positive and negative disruptive changes. To make sense of the interactions between these uncertainties, I have used a systems view to identify the key phenomena at play, and a driving forces scenarios methodology to explore the alternative futures and resulting policy options that might unfold.

Systems View

The immediately noticeable phenomena are the occurrence of the pandemic and subsequent containment lockdown as its primary influences. What is likely to come from these, based on economic logic, is a litany of possible outcomes whose architecture easily mimics a futures wheel, a tool proposed by Jerome Glenn.[17]

The secondary effects include supply chain disruption, labor demobilization (unemployment), diminished incomes, and commodity shortages. Tertiary consequences include inflation, a worsening balance of payments, and rising national debt. Future possible outcomes include a fallback to subsistence agricultural production, a rise in informal economic activities, and growing socio-political tensions.

Whether the potential consequences indicated above actually pan out depends on policy choices made internally by national governments and globally by larger economically influential nations and institutions. The presence, timing, and strength of prevention and remedial actions against economic setbacks are critical uncertainties.

Which Way Africa?

As a result of the pandemic, many African economies slipped in and out of recession; the hope is that these will not develop into a longer-term and more regional depression. Critical here is the interplay of two major driving forces:

- The domestic policy of typical African nations, and
- The global stance of external economic actors and institutions.

When mapped against each other, the interplay of these two forces offers a spectrum of four possible 2025 scenarios, as described below.

Living on the Edge (Strong-Arm Domestic Policy, Supportive Global Stance)

Here, the tendency is to maintain policies adopted under the emergency, when people tolerated drastic actions to save their lives. The now familiar mantra of "respect authority" enshrouds nations as their political saviors facilitate further accumulation of authoritarian governmental powers and reinforce the pull of the past. Maintenance of such power would be buttressed by fiscal support from a friendly global environment. However, most citizens yearn for greater freedom and their potentially reactions, with further malaise, socio-economic stress, potential radicalization, and periodic riots. Many nations have razor's edge stability.

Trouble in Paradise (Strong-Arm Domestic Policy, Hostile Global Stance)

Here, most countries across Africa are ignored by the international community, which emerged from the pandemic weakened and focused on domestic affairs, including a threat of "who-done-it" global conflict. Poorly governed countries persist with strong-arm dictatorial policies inherited from the pandemic era control-oriented decrees.

Many industries haven't recovered from the effects of lockdown. Shocks induced by cuts in foreign investment and aid lead to currency depreciation and galloping inflation. These make it difficult to provide good education, healthcare, and key public services. People resort to informal gray economy activities and subsistence agriculture as survival strategies. Corruption and lawlessness reign and many economies nosedive. Several African nations descend into anarchical societies.

Self-Reliance (Enabling Domestic Policy, Hostile Global Stance)

Across Africa, nations respond to global marginalization challenges with a policy coined by historian Arthur Toynbee as, "stimulus to a society after this society has already broken down."[18] Self-reliance drives everyone—youth, and adults of all ages—backed by enabling governance. Social and human capital blooms, savings rise to boost investment all round, and many African nations recover from recession in preparation for take-off into upper-middle income status.

Horn of Plenty (Enabling Domestic Policy, Supportive Global Stance)

There is a confluence of enabling domestic policies and a supportive global environment, leading toward a more abundant future for the region. The culture of remote working and cashless transactions has flourished. Consequently, the cost of doing business has fallen. Technology boosts productivity, incomes, and education. There is increasingly affordable healthcare for all, building on the infrastructure developed to deal with the pandemic. Things are looking up. Africa can finally start to claim its place in the 21st Century.

Next Steps

These scenarios and those of other futures thinkers can serve as a reference. They offer a range of policy options and outcomes for countries across Africa. The challenge is to develop a shared national vision. The key is turning them into strategies, flexible enabling actions, and a range of delivery tactics to operationalize ambition and opportunity. This would be a significant milestone in not wasting a crisis.

- *What are the likely longer-term effects of social distancing on traditional cultural practices in developing nations?*
- *How have lockdowns impacted social capital and trust?*
- *How can we operationalize optimistic ambitions and visions for developing nations hardest hit by the pandemic?*

Leopold P. Mureithi is a professor of Economics at the University of Nairobi. He consults on technology, employment, and development and co-chairs Kenya's Millennium Project Node. His clients include the UNDP, African Union, and Development Bank of Southern Africa.

Greece 2025—If Only We Knew

By Epaminondas Christophilopoulos

How can the government and companies of Greece "hear the future" and take action to be successful in the post-pandemic era?

This chapter explores a possible 2025 scenario for an already struggling Greece five years after the emergence of the pandemic. In early 2020, Greece had just started to recover from a decade-long deep economic crisis that shrunk GDP and shook the national social fabric. However, the recovery had not led to the much-needed structural reforms, neither had it changed the "live for today Yo no sé mañana"[19] decision-making culture which is intrinsic to the nation's psyche. Nevertheless, the majority of the people were optimistic that the days of austerity were gone for good, and a bright future was ahead.

In the space of a few months, the new center-right government had performed some minor reforms, but mainly managed to create confidence in society, which had an immediate effect on the economy and especially in the key sectors of tourism and energy. Aegean Airlines, the biggest airline in the country, invested in 46 new A320neo aircraft and permissions were granted for some gigantic new hotels.

Major infrastructure investments were also starting to materialize. Fraport, owner of 14 airports in the country, had also just started a

€330 million investment for development work. In the energy field, the prime minister had announced the closure of all lignite plants by 2028, while international oil companies were competing for drilling rights in the Aegean and Ionian Seas. In parallel, Greece, Cyprus, Israel, and the US had agreed on the EastMed plan to build a new, US$7 billion, 1,900km long, natural gas pipeline project to connect the gas reserves of the Eastern Mediterranean to Greece.

If Only We Knew

That was then. Now, five years after the start of the great pandemic crisis, Greece is a different country. The tourism industry has collapsed, along with construction, real estate, and the sale of luxury products and services. On the other hand, digitalization services, primary production (especially agri-food), and a range of novel "reuse" services have flourished.

In the beginning, we thought that everything would return to normal in a few months, but in reality, the pandemic caught the whole country off guard. The immediate effect was an economic crisis that affected all sectors but had a greater impact on tourism, air transport, the construction sector, real estate, the oil industry, performing arts, and professional sports. This in turn created a domino effect for the whole economy. Still, we were optimistic. We had recently experienced a ten-year-long financial crisis, so there was some confidence we could address the new problems in an efficient manner.

At that moment, we could not yet anticipate the more complex, indirect, and longer-term impacts of the pandemic crisis. During the lockdown periods, one could initially only leave home for very few reasons, like visiting a doctor, going to the supermarket, or for a walk. During this time, people re-appreciated the value of a walk in the woods, playing board games with family and friends, reading a forgotten book, trying different types of art, and becoming DIY masters. People also started to re-discover the happiness hidden in simple things, such as face-to-face small talk with friends (initially through video calls), a long walk in the rain, and digging and caring for a small urban garden. Who really needed new clothes when we hardly required any clothes at all, cosmetics, a car, or plastic surgery in this strange new reality?

At the time, and although Greece had a low digitalization performance, the private sector rapidly reorganized, established new work processes, and evolved an ethos based on trust and deliverables instead of time control. Tele-service provision prospered, ranging from tele-sales to tele-teaching of everything from languages and art to fitness to gardening. "Tomorrow belongs to those who can hear it coming," was the slogan David Bowie coined to promote the album *Heroes* back in the 1970s.

Unfortunately, during the early post-pandemic years, we were still incapable of hearing or reading the signals of a rapid shift in values and behaviors that ultimately transformed the global business environment. The elements of the new ethos that everybody was talking about in the 2010s, gradually informed popular culture among the global youth but also gained appeal in older generations.

Today in 2025, "sustainability, self-sufficiency, and social accountability," are known as the 3 S's and are central to public and private policies. Society has shifted sharply toward sustainable production and reuse. Furthermore, there is no access to project funding for companies not complying with the golden 3S principles. To secure financing, it is an absolute must to demonstrate that it will be used for impact investments that deliver broader social or environmental benefits alongside financial returns.

As expected, mass tourism was almost entirely eliminated, while the growth of domestic tourism, and the rise of independent and bleisure (business + leisure) travelers, only partially made up for the losses. The breakdown and restructuring of tourism also affected the construction sector and real estate markets, while retail also collapsed, especially fast fashion. Today, consumers are leaning toward hyperlocalism and various DIY movements.

Urban agriculture is thriving, as well as new lab-stores that provide a quick facelift to your old clothes. The energy sector has not escaped the disruption. Post-pandemic crude oil prices have never exceeded US$60 per barrel, staying substantially lower than pre-crisis levels, so all the planned fossil fuel investments in the country are not viable anymore and have halted.

Now, several renewable energy concepts have been kicked off, such as SMEs renting urban surfaces around cities for distributed energy production, while many rural areas have achieved energy self-sufficiency, which is now a national goal by 2040.

Today, five years after the crisis, Europe is still struggling to adapt in the new reality and return to growth. Inequalities between the European south and north have increased, but so have solidarity movements: Eurozone countries have taken bold actions to jointly address public debt. At least now, it seems that we are better equipped to "hear" the future, plus the 3 S's culture has sparked hope. Nevertheless, as only five years have passed, it is still too early to say whether Greece is on a path to a more sustainable, economically viable, and inclusive future.

- *What possible transformations and "black swan" events are your organization factoring into its thinking and contingency plans for the post-pandemic era?*
- *How are you using scenario planning in the construction of robust strategies to address various plausible futures?*
- *What approach is your organization taking to develop futures literacy to address challenges and opportunities beyond the "official future"?*

Epaminondas Christophilopoulos is the UNESCO chair in Futures Research, and head of the Foresight and Tools Unit in the Hellas Foundation for Research and Technology (FORTH), Greece.

SOCIETY AND LIFESTYLES

Exploring New Normal Futures

By Patrick van der Duin and Hans Stavleu

How might social and psychological factors shape the new normal of post-pandemic society?

The pandemic presented an unusual situation, a gross departure from what we were used to. For example, for many, working or learning from home using digital technology is still not an ideal solution. We miss the whiteboard, the Post-it notes on the wall, the jokes in the hallway, and arguments about last night's TV or football. Around the world, in many countries, the pandemic led to central school exams being abolished and children's study material thrown across the digital fence with the motto: "There you are, now find out for yourself." Pupils, students, and parents all had to adapt to the new situation and create new anchor points and rhythms within a very short time frame.

Many people say that they want nothing more than to return to the old situation. But is that really what we want? And is it even possible? Can the old times be revived and if they can, how do we prevent further outbreaks of infection?

Most of us did not see this coming and, as a result, we were poorly prepared for the resulting health emergency. When we compare this pandemic with the global financial crisis—which started in 2008 with the fall of Lehman Brothers—it's clear that we failed to listen to the warning signs then and have repeated those anticipatory errors now. In 2007, economists warned us about the dangerous consequences of the bad mortgage market in the US. At the end of 2019, health experts warned of the imminent pandemic.

So, what now? When there are still high numbers of deaths and millions of infections worldwide, perhaps it is a little premature or cynical to look ahead and try to think about the period after the pandemic. However, there is little a futures researcher can do about the current situation once the crisis had started. Instead, now is the perfect time to reflect on how we can reshape our society and prevent the next crisis. We need to improve our ability to see the warning signs. This is where futures research can add most value.

Drivers for Tomorrow

Around the world, many countries will possibly look quite different after the crisis. For example, while the Dutch place great value on what they call "acting normal," this will not be the normal to which we were accustomed, but a "new normal." To explore that new normal, we identify key psychological and social components in people's behavior that could have the greatest bearing on how the new normal plays out.

In psychological terms, people can be divided into two groups— firstly those who want to take control of the situation, make their own choices, and ensure their own survival. Then there are those who are resigned to their situation and leave the crisis management to the "higher powers"—control versus resignation. Then, with regard to the social component, people can be divided into those who like to take matters into their own hands and those who prefer to work together—solitary versus solidarity. Based on these two dimensions, we define four possible normal scenarios for the future after the crisis:

The New Normal: back to the future–Driven by solitary and controlled behavior, this new normal is characterized by societal fragmentation, technological acceleration, and an increasingly global market.

The Different Normal: be yourself–Driven by solitary and acquiescent behavior with characteristics that include a desire for autonomy, with people becoming more self-sufficient and increasingly nationalistic.

The Old Normal: business as usual–Driven by resignation and solidarity. This future is very similar to the past we left behind in 2019, with the welfare state taking care of its citizens, a thriving economy, and an expanding European market.

The Normal Normal: back to basics–Driven by control and solidarity. This is a future in which people tend to reflect on themselves often, and which has a focus on small-scale and local activities.

In the **New Normal**, society is in a state of permanent alertness, with everyone and everything under surveillance, all the time. If necessary, people are willing to sacrifice their privacy, because being able to respond to potential or actual threats requires immediate access to data. To that end, people and organizations use the latest technology and have access to a worldwide network of experts, allowing everything and everyone to be mobilized quickly in the event of a viral contamination or other crisis.

Different Normal is a world in permanent ignorance. People try to live autonomously and limit their interaction with others, producing an egocentric kind of existence. People acquire the ability to fix things themselves and understand the value of things they have. In the event of most major types of health challenge or environmental crises, nations immediately close their borders to the outside world.

The **Old Normal** is all about convenience, with society in a permanent state of comfort. The government tries to take care of everyone and there are excellent social safety nets in case something unpleasant happens. The extensive provision of financial care makes people relatively lazy. On the other hand, in the event of a crisis, the best experts the country has to offer and, if necessary, foreign experts can be called upon immediately.

The **Normal Normal** society focuses primarily on local issues and preventive healthcare. Everything revolves around producing, working, and organizing at a small-scale local level. In the event of a crisis, personal healthcare and fitness are used as survival tools. As a result of a large-scale reassessment of our values, among our top priorities now are trust, sustainability, transparency, and credibility.

Synthesis

Regardless of the outcome, the future will not be what it used to be. The future could be either one of the four narratives outlined above or, more likely, a combination of all of them. In addition to the aspects of human behavior that we divided into a psychological and a social component, culture will also play an important role. As we look across the world, we can already see that the key determinants of viral spread, impacts, response measures, and possible exit strategies are often culturally determined.

As far as the Netherlands is concerned, we see the following. Although the Old Normal provides the best match with the Dutch national character, we would argue that the Netherlands should not pursue this scenario because that would mean we will have learned too little from this crisis. The Different Normal, on the other hand, appears to be at odds with the national character of the open society that we are or should be.

We expect the continuing social and political discussion in the Netherlands to revolve around what we have outlined as the New Normal and Normal Normal. For the former to occur, the country will have to expand its innovative capabilities and encourage entrepreneurship. For the latter, the current crisis is primarily a period of reflection and learning. The most important conclusion in this scenario is that we must return to a smaller and more local level of activity and organization.

To avoid having to live through a similar crisis again, we need to think about how we can respond to future crises. Decision will be required on whether the guiding principles are adapting our behavior (the Normal Normal), closing ourselves off (the Different Normal), using data (the New Normal), or letting government act on our behalf (the Old Normal).

The current crisis also throws a different light on the relationship between people and science, because we do not know whether science was the cause of or will be the solution to the crisis. Finally, we expect the main social impact of the crisis to be how we deal with our personal and social healthcare: will protective masks become the new airbags or looked back on as some silly gadget from a recent past?

- *What are the critical lessons we should learn from the pandemic if we are to prevent future crises?*
- *How might the relationship between humans and science evolve as a result of the crisis?*
- *What impact could this pandemic have on how we make contingency plans for future health emergencies?*

Patrick van der Duin is managing director of the Stichting Toekomstbeeld der Techniek. He previously worked at KPN Research, Delft University of Technology, and Fontys University of Applied Sciences. He has a PhD in foresight and innovation.

Hans Stavleu is the lead future explorer at curiozy.net. He previously worked for KPN Research and TNO, a Dutch research organization. He was also an associate professor in foresight and education at Leiden Hogeschool.

Lockdown Legacy: How the Pandemic Could Inspire Individual Ownership of Physical Activity

By Dr. Adam Hawkey

Looking back at the pandemic from 2025, what legacy has been left regarding our attitude toward physical activity?

As we look back from 2025, it is clear that the pandemic that started in 2020 had a profound impact on our lives. It was devastating for many in regards to loss of life, long-term illness, financial hardship, and mental health. Lockdowns and strict measures of physical distancing reduced engagement in activities long promoted by the scientific community for their health and wellbeing benefits.

In the lockdowns, partly due to the closing of gyms and fitness centers, it became necessary to find new ways to stay active. Individuals who owned training equipment such as exercise bikes, treadmills, and weight training devices were able to continue with some form of normal routine. Those without such luxuries were encouraged to convert tins of baked beans, bags of rice or flour, and bottled water into dumbbell and kettle bell substitutes—some even used their own children.

Impact of the Lockdown on Physical Activity

The lockdown provided medical practitioners, sports scientists, and fitness professionals with the opportunity to promote the benefits of physical activity on a previously incomprehensible scale. It became apparent that exercise behaviors were starting to change. Studies conducted during the early stages of the outbreak in the UK, by Sport England and Nuffield Health, revealed that more than half of those surveyed (59%) were going for a walk as part of their allocated daily activity time. Encouragingly, 81% of responders stated that they would try to continue with their new exercise regime once life returned to a "new normal."

Most significant was that the lockdown and the threat of infection in general, led people to recognize the link between keeping active and staying physically and mentally healthy. The studies found that nearly two thirds (63%) of adults were reported to have said that it was more important to be active now, compared with before the pandemic. Even more people (67%) believed that exercise had a noticeable improvement on their mental health.

Post-Pandemic Progress: Physical Activity in 2025

Now in 2025, five years after the initial lockdowns, our way of thinking and our practice of physical activity has changed even further. There remains an appetite for using gyms and fitness centers—these are still the only places for most to utilize high-end specialist training equipment. There is also still demand for leisure centers, because these facilities provide access to resources such as swimming pools, squash courts, and climbing walls. These establishments also continue to offer face-to-face social interaction; something that was missing during the lockdowns.

However, for many, the lockdowns inspired daily training at home, in the garden, or during the often limited time allowed out of the house. It not only became a temporary refuge from the negative aspects of confinement, but actually transitioned into a way of life. It became a habit, almost an addiction, for the feel-good euphoria that many describe accompanying exercise. As we sit here now—five years post the start of the pandemic—exercising and looking after physical and mental health have never been a more integral part of our daily existence.

For years, perhaps even decades, scientists and health professionals had been preaching about the benefits of keeping active, but society as a whole, had not been listening; evidenced by hospital admissions for obesity related treatment in England reaching a record of more than a million in the year leading up to the pandemic. With being overweight identified as one of the most significant risk factors for the severest forms of viral infection during the pandemic, people were forced to take note. Hence, the numbers of those engaging in a range of physical activity pursuits has increased dramatically. As a consequence of the unprecedented platform to promote the benefits of keeping active provided by the virus, the lockdown taught society to take individual ownership of physical activity levels.

Within five years of the outbreak, the landscape of keeping active has changed. Families can regularly be seen in the park, playing a game of tag together. People are using their cars less and parking further away from work to increase their daily steps. Government schemes designed to promote cycling to work have been expanded, further encouraging individuals to travel under their own power. Society's interaction with technology has also evolved. The use of advanced wearable technology is now commonplace, allowing accurate monitoring of vital individualized health and fitness data.

Companies have also made a noticeable contribution to the culture of "movement is medicine" by reducing activities that traditionally involved being sedentary. An increase in the provision of standing desks, the encouragement of walking meetings, and promotion of active lunch breaks have helped to reduce the amount of time spent sitting down, especially for those working from home.

The combined result of all these lifestyle changes is a reduction in the incidence and severity of conditions such as heart disease, diabetes, obesity, stroke, and some cancers. Without such a seismic shift in attitudes and behavior toward physical activity, these conditions would undoubtably have resulted in greater levels of morbidity and mortality throughout the world.

The Lasting Legacy of the Lockdown

While the pandemic was devastating in so many ways, it had a lasting and positive impact on the mindset of millions of people. The lockdowns experienced across the world forged the future for our current attitudes and behavior toward exercise and physical activity. With the support of governments, employers, and the medical and scientific communities, this allowed people to take greater ownership of their own health and wellbeing. Perhaps the most striking and lasting legacy of the lockdowns is that, in 2025, individuals feel more inspired and empowered to engage in exercise and physical activity than ever before.

- *Why did it take such a devastating pandemic for people to understand the importance of exercise and physical activity to health and wellbeing?*
- *Will a shift in understanding and practice of personal responsibility for healthcare lead to a more proactive rather than reactive approach to health, wellbeing, and medicine?*
- *What does the future hold for the development of new ways to exercise?*

Dr Adam Hawkey is associate professor of Sports Science and Human Performance at Solent University Southampton, professor of Sports Science and Medicine at the Saveetha Institute of Medical and Technical Sciences (SIMATS) in India, and an honorary lecturer within the University of Dundee's School of Medicine. He is a leading expert in the exchange of scientific knowledge relating to the enhancement of human health and performance.

The Digital Health Passport

By Leland A. Shupp

How can we best balance the need for robust public health with the desire for personal freedom, privacy, and equality of opportunity?

The year is 2025. After suffering over one million pandemic-related deaths, the US has changed significantly since the outbreak of the virus. There is renewed emphasis on science and medical expertise. The population's tolerance for politically motivated suppression of science has declined, and many political hacks have been removed from federal agencies. The Center for Disease Control and Prevention (CDC) has regained much of the respect and prestige lost in the Trump era.

The US is once again an active participant in the World Health Organization (WHO) and is slowly regaining its leadership role in global health. The Gates Foundation's commitment to global health initiatives has helped bolster the reputation of the US considerably, and remained engaged and active even during the isolationist and antagonistic Trump years.

The pandemic hit the US hard as health experts and politicians endlessly argued about the need to shelter in place versus the need for economic activity. This resulted in the pandemic hitting the US in successive waves. The first wave hit in spring 2020, and the second wave quickly followed in summer 2020, as states opened too early, resulting in a surge of new infections after Memorial Day Weekend. The third wave hit in the winter of 2020 and, much like the Spanish flu of 1919, this wave was much more lethal than the first. Successive waves of more virulent virus variants have followed each year since, killing thousands more and forcing constant revisions to vaccine development and social distancing measures.

The US government makes heroic and expensive efforts to contain the ongoing pandemic, but states often have their own agendas, which may or may not align with federal priorities and practices. In Democratic states and cities there is strong alignment with the federal government, and an emphasis on following federal guidelines and scientific recommendations. In many Republican controlled states and locales there is still strong resistance to federal oversight and mistrust of science. As a result, laws and guidelines are often ignored, resulting in much higher rates of infection, hospitalization, and death. In these areas, the negative health outcomes are often attributed to the hand of God, or to conspiracy theories.

Republican enclaves don't prioritize vaccination, social distancing, or mask wearing. There are no restrictions on public events. Personal independence trumps the social good, and it comes at a high cost. This resistance to federal regulation and scientific consensus creates strong friction between different regions of the US. Resistance runs rampant in rural areas, the South, and much of the Midwest. In contrast, the heavily populated coastal areas and most large population centers tend to follow federal guidelines and emphasize scientific recommendations. For the remainder of this article, I will focus upon the social system that has emerged in this scenario within highly populated, socially liberal, and Democratic-leaning areas of the US.

A bifurcated class system has emerged, with two classes of citizens in the most heavily populated areas of the US. One class has antibodies to the current strains of the virus; the other does not. People who have tested positive for the antibodies to the latest virus variants have complete freedom of movement and the ability to do almost anything that they want to. The "Vaxxed" can work in bustling offices, exercise in packed gyms, eat in crowded restaurants, and attend sold out sports and entertainment events in gigantic stadiums.

The Vaxxed must show proof of the latest vaccine and/or a confirmed positive test for the antibody, which can be required in any public setting. Those who can't show proof are treated harshly with immediate removal, mandatory quarantine in converted jails, and high fines. This new class system is rigorously enforced for the public good.

People who have not been vaccinated face highly restricted movement in many places. These "Anti-Vaxxers" are required to work from home, exercise in virtual classes, pick up their takeout food from the back doors of restaurants, and watch cultural events from afar. Anti-Vaxxers have highly restricted participation in the outside world, even as that world roars back to life.

As more people contract the virus and medical databases grow, population sub-segments are categorized as especially vulnerable to the virus. Quantitative modeling becomes key as a means of identifying vulnerable Anti-Vaxxers, and these newly identified "Vulnerables" are rarely thrilled at being outed by artificial intelligence models.

Being an Anti-Vaxxer can mean stigma and ridicule along with the constraints of "living in place." Anti-Vaxxers face monitored movement, special shopping hours, and live life mostly within the confines of the home. This has led to an increase in mental health issues, growing from the 30% reported at the onset of shelter-in-place orders to over 65% currently among this group. Depression, domestic violence, and divorce are all up among vulnerable Anti-Vaxxers.

As the virus mutates, and new and more dangerous natural and man-made viruses appear, medical authorities quickly realize the need for a more comprehensive solution than simply showing proof of a recent vaccine. They make the case before Congress, which enacts the Digital Health Passport Act of 2024 despite strong Republican opposition.

The US Health Passport comprises a digital file with a comprehensive list of current vaccinations and known antibodies for each citizen. It has location awareness and contact tracing features. It is required for air travel and to drive across state lines. Doctors are required to update the passport when giving vaccinations, so that any citizen's current vaccination status can be viewed both online and in the Digital Health Passport app itself. Individual data is fed into a national database, which enables health authorities to understand quickly where Vulnerables or non-compliant citizens reside and go.

The Anti-Vaxx Movement, fed by false information provided by alternative health "experts" and state sponsored misinformation campaigns, fights hard against the idea of a Digital Health Passport. These activists work hard to undermine the system with armed protests, fake passports, and false alarms. Health clinics are targeted by anonymous bombers. Falsified passports are bought and sold on the black market. Bots attack CDC servers with misinformation, reporting outbreaks and disease clusters where none exist.

Despite the resistance, the high death toll of the pandemic creates widespread public support for the Digital Health Passport, and debate begins about making it cover much more of each person's health data. The government commandeers genetic data from genomic information banks (e.g. Ancestry.com, 23&Me) and incorporates this information into the passports, further dividing the population into enclaves according to their health issues and risks. This creates a further stratified society where freedom, power, and privilege are based on government assessment of both current health condition and potential health risks. It seems only a matter of time before other genetic information becomes the basis for classification, division, segmentation, and segregation.

- *How can we be more agile and effective in preventing the spread of contagious diseases and viruses?*
- *How can we best balance the need for public health with the desire for personal privacy?*
- *What personal privacy compromises should we accept in the face of high risk and rising mortality rates, and how can they be undone?*

Leland A. Shupp has been helping companies identify new growth opportunities for products, services, and brands for 20+ years. He integrates customer insights with foresight, design thinking, and advanced analytics to help companies grow and prosper.

Generational Games: Age Cohort Reactions to the Pandemic

By Arthur Weiss

How might millennials, Gen Z, and other generations respond to the post-pandemic period?

The 1920s were unusual in that the generation reaching adulthood saw both the end of the First World War and the impact of Spanish flu infecting over a quarter of the world population. Those alive then experienced a period of massive change resulting from these two factors. Women received the vote in the US and much of Europe. In Asia, there was the start of national independence movements. Despite the Roaring Twenties post-war boom, the decade ended with the depression that extended from the Wall Street Crash in 1929 to the mid-1930s and beyond, accompanied by the rise of totalitarian rule across parts of Europe.

One hundred years later, the common factor is a new pandemic combined with a severe global economic downturn, and the background of recent and ongoing conflicts across the world. So, this time round, how might different generations across society behave after the pandemic that started rolling across the planet in 2020?

The Silent Generation (1928-1945)

The Silent Generation, born between 1928 and 1945, already have limited influence except on their descendants. Contemplating their mortality, the pandemic is likely to have little immediate impact on the lives of most unless it tipped them over the brink into financial insecurity. However, in more affluent countries, an eventual release from shielding and lockdown should let many in this cohort celebrate, making the most of the years left to them. No longer homebodies, visiting children and grandchildren will remain important. Many may also gain a new zest for life, leading to business opportunities for travel and holidays targeted at this age group.

Baby Boomers (1946-c1963)

In many Western countries in particular, Baby Boomers will be nearing retirement or already retired. As a generation in the West, their formative years were spent during the "cold war." This, combined with the lingering impacts of World War Two, means that many in this generation still see the world as "us" and "them," distrusting the "global village," as seen in conservative voting patterns in many nations. This perspective will likely remain, but unlike the previous generation, this group may continue to increase their spending in the post-pandemic period.

The Baby Boomer mindset may be one of making the most of their remaining years before the global apocalypse they thought had been avoided with the fall of the Berlin Wall. One implication of a Boomer spending spree could be to leave a smaller inheritance for their Millennial children. Some may also become increasingly resentful and even fearful—as the "new normal" replaces everything they had believed about how the world works. In contrast, some might relish the new opportunities presented by video communication and the growing penetration of digital technologies into everyday life.

Gen X (c1964-c1980)

Around the world, Gen X have been particularly hard-hit by the pandemic. Caring for aging parents and Gen Z children, those in work may count themselves lucky. Many will have lost jobs or savings, with future hopes and dreams evaporating. Those in work may feel nervous and look for scapegoats. This could be reflected in votes for populist politicians who hark back to a past that has gone, as well as a growing belief in conspiracies that get amplified across social media. This generation might well wish for the "old normal" and so be increasingly conservative and risk averse—distrusting new ways of working, changing societal attitudes such as the rise of environmentalism, and even some technologies.

Millennials / Gen Y (c1981–c1993)

This generation grew up to embrace the Internet and so will have been particularly shaken by the pandemic. They saw the impact of 9/11 and the "war against terror" which many viewed as racist, wasteful, and wrong. They may blame their parents' generation, yet lack the same level of enthusiasm that Gen Z has for activism. In debt and uncertain about their futures, they may increasingly resent new leisure patterns of their parents—knowing an outcome may be their failing to inherit Baby Boomer wealth. This could lead to family splits with Millennials rejecting their parents and "going it alone." Lacking financial security, they might seek other forms of happiness—including social media interactions and peer-group agreement about how their world has been damaged by previous generations.

Unlike their elders, and sharing characteristics with Gen Z, social interactions may depend increasingly on technology, but unlike Gen Z, these connections are likely to be more transient. Essentially, this generation will have been affected by the pandemic in ways that are different from those who preceded them, as it may have removed further hope for stability. Reactions could well echo those of similar generations following the 1920 Spanish flu epidemic—and so this generation might try to live life to the fullest but lack the financial wherewithal to do so fully.

Gen Z (c1994–c2012)

Many Gen Zs have embraced environmental activism and social awareness to a greater degree than Generations X and Y. The pandemic will have resulted in interrupted education for most of this cohort, with the oldest just graduating or starting work and younger members still at school. This generation may have seen parents out of work, or working from home, with their pre-pandemic lives turned upside down. Whereas before 2020 activism was viewed as important, Gen Z are increasingly likely to believe that the world needs to change at a fundamental level and that they should fight for this.

They share similarities with those born 100 years earlier—the "flapper generation"—but may be less carefree and experiential, especially as most won't have the relief of the end of a war to celebrate. Lacking experience, they could also leave themselves open to those making the most noise and flock to extremism—political, environmental, and possibly social as well. Some may become increasingly rebellious, joining protest groups on the left and right, fighting against values they identify with the "old normal." Having been shut in, they will likely seek to get out—and, unlike Millennials, physical connections, mediated by technology, could be important.

Gen Alpha (c2013–c2025)

Gen Alpha—still at school—were born after 2012. In the future, they may question the value of an education that can be disrupted so easily. They will also see the angst of their parents. The impacts on this generation of the pandemic, and several months out of the classroom, are unlikely to be fully seen for a decade or more.

However, parental and other adult uncertainties are likely to lead to increased insecurity and mental health problems as the older members of this cohort leave primary education and enter their teenage years and adulthood. This might feed back to younger siblings, so adult Gen Alphas are likely to be very different to previous generations. They may parallel their equivalents 100–120 years ago, who also grew up during a period of technological innovation (radio, telephone), global income inequality, and social turmoil.

Summary

The response to the 2020 pandemic over the next two to five years will not be homogenous. Generations will respond differently based on their prior experiences—and despite common factors across the world, there will also be some regional differences in behaviors. Long-term impacts may be minimal in the behavior of the older age groups—those born prior to 1960–1965. The greatest financial impact will likely be on those born from 1965 to 1980, who could become concerned about their future. This may also feed into the Millennials, born after 1980, who may take more risks because of a lack of certainty and a sense of less to lose. In contrast, Gen Z could look to change the world—even more than now, with activism of various types becoming the norm.

- *How might those born prior to 1965 view their futures inthe post-pandemic period?*
- *Gen Alpha are starting school or finishing primary school during the pandemic, how might their disrupted education impact their transition to adulthood?*
- *Could Gen Z parallel the Flapper Generation of the 1920s, since both survived a pandemic, economic turbulence, and large-scale warfare?*

Arthur Weiss is CEO of AWARE. He has consulted for companies globally and led workshops on strategy, scenario planning, and competitive intelligence.

Social Distancing: A Cultural Analysis of the Post-Pandemic World

By Kevin Jae

What kind of culture could emerge as the world struggles to adapt to the concept of social distancing and how might this impact relationships between individuals within the nation, and between nations?

Pandemics are not inevitable. The 2019–20 virus outbreak achieved pandemic status in part because of the structures of our globalized world and our megacities. The virus spread from a single Chinese city to the rest of the world in a matter of weeks; would this still have happened if instead most people lived in small, isolated agrarian communities? This chapter is a speculative endeavor. It aims to analyze social distancing as an emerging aspect of our culture and post-pandemic lifestyles and explore the potential impacts on individual behaviors and societal structures.

A new cultural logic has emerged to fight the virus: social distancing. According to this concept, each individual has an imaginary, hygienic bubble that is between one and two meters in radius. When an outsider penetrates the bubble, there is a risk of contagion. Even with familiar faces, friends, and family we are all considered a risk. Our families and social circles are transformed into potential threats.

Social distancing is not an action that is only performed by individuals. There are bubbles at all levels of society, where variations of this logic apply. Groups of people that live together—whether family members or housemates—can form their own bubble, jealously guarding the interior of the bubble from those outside. When someone or something from the external world infiltrates, the bubble becomes compromised. This logic has been adopted by many nation-states as well. To prevent infection, the national community (the "national bubble") secures itself by protecting national borders. As a result, the pandemic has led to many canceled flights and restrictions on the entry of foreigners.

The logic of social distancing constructs two types of culturally imagined spaces. There is the interior space. This space is imagined as clean, safe, and above all, it is free of the virus. Then there is the exterior space, or the world outside the bubble. This space holds the danger of contagion, where infected things and persons wander around, potentially spewing viral pathogens into the air.

Interactions with people and objects in the external space requires an identification and assessment of risk. The differentiation of interior and exterior space is a subjective judgment: one person's home is another person's hostile territory. Mediating between the interior space and the exterior space are the orifices (especially the nostrils and the mouth), the thresholds into a home or building, and the ports of entry into a country. These entryways are what ultimately protect the orderly interior from the chaotic exterior.

How might this cultural logic change society three years down the line? The following scenario makes two assumptions. Firstly, in the post-pandemic world, the virus is present in every country across the globe and new more virulent strains continue to emerge. Secondly, an effective vaccine that works across all variants has not yet been developed and vaccinations rates vary dramatically within and between countries. Hence, variations of social distancing measures are a constant necessity.

It is the year 2023, the third year that the specter of the pandemic has haunted the world. We are following an average day of a typical individual in his 30s. We can call him Dennis. He spends the first couple of hours of the day locked in his room on the 38th floor—virtual tools allow him to work in the sanctuary of his home and away from the enclosed office space, where he once worked with a group of co-workers.

When he finishes his workday, Dennis puts on his mask, and heads out of his apartment complex. It is a Friday, but no one appears to be in a festive mood. There are hardly any groups with more than three people visible, and everyone is wearing a mask to protect themselves from invisible, pathogenic microdroplets. He has made plans to visit a group of friends today.

To obtain the privilege of entrance into a grocery store, Dennis is assessed by a masked security guard who measures his temperature, checks his digital identification, and supervises Dennis as he disinfects his hands with soap and water. The digital identification is mandatory in public spaces for proper risk assessment. This tracks where the identity holder lives, where he or she has been, and who they might have been in contact with. These powerful surveillance tools track the movement of all citizens to determine their risk levels.

If Dennis lives near a recent virus cluster or has been in contact with an infected individual, his digital identification will confirm this. If his risk levels are too high, then he may be refused entry. In 2023, individuals are defined by their risk levels and vaccination status—the more regularly you have been jabbed, the greater your freedoms. Dennis has seen news reports of people who have become ostracized by family members due to high risk levels and a reluctance to be vaccinated. As he leaves the grocery store, the security guard ensures that he disinfects his hands once more.

Dennis arrives at his friends' apartment complex. He lines up to be tested for entry into the building; his temperature and digital identification are checked once more. Personal relations are not as easy and casual as before. Dennis and his friends only meet in small groups now. They almost never hang out in public spaces like restaurants and bars.

Dennis washes his hands and finally taps elbows with his friends in greeting. They sit on the couch with at least a meter's distance between them—they are wary of swapping microdroplets.

Once again, the topic of conversation turns into empty plans for travel. Unfortunately, multiple new viral variants and clusters had re-emerged recently, both in their country and several others. As a result, most nations had adopted even stricter border control and quarantine procedures. Casual tourists from their country were on the red "no entry" list for most destinations and effectively grounded as a result. Even if they could travel, a two-week quarantine awaits them on destination arrival and return.

It comes time to leave; Dennis will probably see this group of friends in a month. They meet more regularly in virtual spaces to play games and watch movies. However, they still place value on the ritual of in-person meetings, even though Dennis knows that his friends will have to disinfect the living room after his departure. As he walks home with his mask on, the streets are quiet and deserted. He passes by an empty public square, where the city used to hold free concerts and events for the public. A man is coughing a couple of meters behind him—Dennis shudders.

- *How will the pandemic change the ways that individuals interact and engage with one another?*
- *Many see the post-pandemic culture as one of separation and borders. Could the virus provoke the opposite response and lead to increased connectivity and solidarity?*
- *What kind of global responses might emerge from a permanent culture of social distancing, and what must nation-states do in response?*

Kevin is a research assistant at the Diversity Institute, Canada. He is a polyglot, an autodidact, an anthropologist, and a futurist.

Great Reset Day 2025

By Caroline Figuères

How might our future wellbeing be impacted by technology?

"In the end, we did pretty well," Johanna said.

"Certainly," Ibrahim replied. "But without you, Yun, and the whole team, we would never have made it! Tomorrow, on February 28th, it will be three years that we have worked together!"

"And great to have an extra day off," Yun said. "I wonder how people will react."

Yun was the most pragmatic of the research group. She had launched the "Hug" movement in 2023. During the first phase of the overwhelming pandemic, most countries on the planet, starting with China, had decided that the best way to fight viral spread was confining people to their homes. In many countries schools were closed for months or more, and people forced to telework if possible. Social distancing became the norm. The virus had claimed directly or indirectly millions of lives worldwide, everywhere, impacting rich and poor, women and men. However, its biggest impacts in Europe were among the elderly and those weakened by co-morbidities. Two years later, it was mainly new virus variants that sparked the emergence of the large-scale Hug movement.

Without having a clear explanation for why, the new waves of infection had proportionally claimed many more victims among younger generations than the earlier pandemic. Some young people, who had made fun of social distancing in 2020, were thankful that these measures were applied in the following years to protect them.

During the 2020-21 pandemic, it was noticed in Europe that individuals found it difficult to keep their distance from each other. It became ever more apparent that humans need to be in physical contact with their loved ones, both for their mental wellbeing and to avoid feelings of isolation. To address the challenge, for three years Johanna, Yun, Ibrahim, and their team had worked tirelessly to change the habits of their fellow human beings through a global program called "Hug." They taught people how to have physical contact while safeguarding their wellbeing through social distancing.

Through subsequent pandemics, people had become so used to overcrowded public transport during rush hours that they ended up silencing their body signals which had previously alerted them when they came too close to danger. In these moments of forced crowding, people mentally isolated themselves. As a result, others around them no longer existed. They did not see or hear or smell them anymore. They preferred denying the presence of others, because to acknowledge their existence created a physical malaise.

Societies also lost the notion of intimate, private, and social distancing, as defined within the study field of proxemics, which is crucial to prevent viral spread. So, during these successive pandemics, viruses could pass easily from one individual to another. Whether the person who carried it died or not was of little significance. It was the infection rate that mattered for the virus' survival. It flourished in crowds.

Hug's basic idea was simple. Johanna applied the technology of car proximity sensors to humans. The Hug sensor, that every human being wore permanently, emitted a signal as soon as another human entered his/her sphere of personal distance, fixed at five feet (1.5 meters). Johanna's work allowed the development of a sensor that gave back to humans the notion of social distance. Simply put, social distance was defined as the distance between two individuals standing face to face, arms stretched horizontally. But as nobody walks around with arms outstretched, the sensor was very useful for relearning distances and worked much better than mobile apps. It seemed that human beings needed a sensor to restore common sense.

There were many models on the market. The basic model looked a bit like a miner's lamp. Across the globe, it had been made available to everyone free of charge. Of course, more sophisticated models existed: some came in the form of a pendant or as a watch, some were integrated into clothing such as hats, bandanas, and veils. Some people had even installed the sensor under their skin. The basic models just indicated the five feet social distance and beeped when you were too close. In Europe, to protect privacy, any connection of this free basic sensor to the Internet was forbidden.

Young people adopted the sensors quickly. Little by little, individuals rediscovered the notion of social distance in public spaces. During recent years, this had also led to modifications of public transport and the development, on a large scale, of teleworking and online education. As a consequence, many people were able to move out of overcrowded cities. However, prohibition of physical contact was not desirable, impossible at one level, and could even become counterproductive. Given the quantity of existing viruses, it was necessary to maintain a certain level of infection to continue to develop antibodies!

This is where Yun had a genius idea. She reinvented the fortnight. For 13 days in a row people used their sensors while going about their business outside their homes. Then, on the fourteenth day, they could choose to deactivate them. On that day, they could approach anyone as close as they wanted, as long as it was consensual. In popular parlance, that day had become "Hug Day". The following day saw the resumption of a fortnight, with respect for social distance, which made it possible to limit the spread of potential viruses.

Hug days became public holidays; twenty-six times a year. The three hundred and sixty-fifth day of the year had therefore become special. Worldwide, people agreed to make it an international holiday, commonly called "Super Hug," and set for February 28th. Calendars all over the world were adapted to reflect this change.

"As usual, tomorrow, for Super Hug Day, we will pay tribute to people who died from successive pandemics and honor high-contact essential workers," Johanna said.

"February 29th, 2025 will be remembered as the Great Reset Day," added Yun, "as our governments will announce that sensors and protective masks are no longer mandatory. Pity that we could not do more research on the effects of the sensors without masks."

"I wonder if I will feel naked when I remove mine for good," Ibrahim said. "Maybe I should grow a beard again!"

Unconsciously, Johanna adjusted her protective mask. She was smiling but nobody noticed.

This scenario raises important issues for society, such as determining ethical limits on the use of technology to improve the individual/human condition. Bigger picture public discussion is also required on the potentially negative, exclusionary consequences of imposing decisions and solutions on whole societies and communities, especially if the latter are governed by majority rule or authoritarian regimes. Perhaps the core challenge is one of developing measures to prevent future outbreaks in a post-pandemic world that do not counterpose the values of human autonomy and social freedom with the need for a healthy, sustainable planet and humankind.

- *How desirable is it for social, political, and ecological problems to increasingly be tackled by the mainly technological solutions of private companies, often in collaboration with nations?*
- *How can we prevent a tendency to tackle global challenges with technological "solutions" led by powerful nations?*
- *How can we move toward preventive measures based in ecological and social justice, that are tackling the causes of pandemics?*

Caroline is a recognized writer who has published and contributed to numerous fiction and non-fiction books and won awards for several short stories. She is a sanitary engineer by education and a consultant with 35 years' experience in water management, information, communication technologies for development, and capacity building.

Nowhere to Hide in 2025

By Gina Clifford

Over the next few years, how might the pandemic era public health monitoring technologies, developed for and by governments and corporations, be used against us?

This chapter presents a fictional "life in 2025" scenario, when the pandemic has passed, but social inequalities it caused are more pervasive than ever. During the pandemic, governments and corporations developed digital health monitoring tools and platforms. Some governments made tracking applications mandatory. Now in 2025, many fear that tracking data is being misused to target and harass certain groups.

All Nigel could think to do was run. Not that it would do much good. Cameras and sensors everywhere continuously betrayed his exact location. Even his face camouflaging lotion couldn't fool the system. With bioacoustics and bone recognition radar they didn't even need to see his face. Nigel's body and bones are his identity. In 2025, law enforcement is now tracking "persons of interest" using drone swarms from the Special Tactical Intercept Corps (STICs).

After some national track and trace solutions failed, and with rising concerns over the ability to monitor the spread of the virus across borders, the need for better international coordination became apparent. Hence, the Centralized Health Office Registration Database (CHORD) was developed in 2022 as part of a more global solution for controlling disease spread. The database started being implemented in some countries and organizations in mid-2022. Because the virus spread so easily, governments wanted to avoid shuttering virtually every business for extended periods as happened in the 2020 and 2021 global lockdowns, causing widespread economic downturns.

"That CHORD hack should have been fool-proof. How did they track me so quickly? I've got to get out of here now. Those STICs will be here soon and then I'm in trouble."

Some economies collapsed almost completely as the pandemic hit already fragile governments, with millions exposed to hunger and homelessness. So, CHORD was implemented hastily with help from the digital sector. Designed to track the health of everyone, everywhere, in real time, CHORD knew if, when, and where you had been vaccinated, infected, or treated, monitoring where you lived and shopped, and predicting your health risks.. CHORD's main job was to warn you if anyone with an active infection was nearby. Governments were eager to implement it because it promised to mitigate the viral spread as borders reopened and travel restrictions lifted globally.

This was all part of international governments' collective 2022 "We Got This" resiliency strategy. And it worked very well. In countries like India, Poland, Israel, China, and some states and corporations in the US, many citizens were required to use some version of CHORD because it was so helpful in monitoring and controlling new outbreaks. At the time, with so much despair and uncertainty, people welcomed the app as a way to safely maintain their normal routines.

Now, in 2025, vaccines are readily available, and there is lots of new research around defeating the next killer virus. However, governments and corporations didn't shelve CHORD. Thanks to near ubiquitous and ever faster 5G networks, CHORD is a powerful digital platform impacting even more of our lives. Several governments require every-one to maintain an active CHORD account for everything from digital passports and driving licenses to voter and citizen ID numbers.

CHORD's sophistication in tracking behavioral metrics, such as how fast we drive and how often we eat at fast-food restaurants, makes 2020-era voice-controlled AI assistants seem like toys. The app is designed to help citizens make healthy choices in all aspects of life. Governments and corporations create strong participatory incentives for citizens to share data with healthcare providers, insurance firms, landlords, the police, consumer product companies, and more.

Nigel was born in 2002, a year after 9/11. He's too young to remember, but grew up learning about the Patriot Act, giving the US government broad powers to search and surveil citizens without permission. It was supposed to prevent terrorism, but as immigrants, Nigel's family members were often harassed by government agents.

As he raced through the streets, a glinting camera lens affixed to the corner of an old bank building caught his eye. It forced him to stop cold as a fresh wave of anxiety arrived. It was the same kind of camera that he used to see in his neighborhood. The same neighborhood where his father was once dragged from his home by police as part of a terrorism investigation. Now it was happening again. The ideological rifts that existed back in 2020 were now more pervasive than ever. People in Nigel's neighborhood were feeling unsafe with CHORD tracking their movements. Will Nigel's family again be targeted by xenophobic officials the way they were after 9/11?

This isn't the end. It is the beginning. Nigel and millions of people around the world just like him are fighting back. And taking down CHORD is just the beginning of this fight.

- *How can we ensure privacy and security of personal information collected by digital platforms designed for disease management?*
- *How might personal data collected for track and trace be used illegally or immorally against minority groups or individuals?*
- *How could technology empower or amplify the impact governments and corporations have on an open society?*

Gina Clifford is the technology communications manager at Jabil, with decades of experience working across technology sectors.

SECTORAL FUTURES

Insurance in the Post-Pandemic World

By David Smith

How has the pandemic impacted an insurance industry that is already being disrupted by digital technologies, InsurTech, new entrants, and an increasingly changing role from compensator to preventer of loss?

Accelerating Digital

New technologies, the increasing availability of real-time data, and consumer expectations were all driving deep-seated change within the insurance industry prior to the pandemic. The gradual shift from compensation to prevention, the penetration of new "InsurTech" ventures, as both partner and competitor, and the broader digitization of the industry were already significant enough trends to master.

Before the pandemic, 2019 research from Deloitte found that one third of insurance executives believed that digital trends would probably leave their organization in a weaker position, or in the extreme, cause them to cease to exist altogether.[20] Accenture's 2018 research found that only 20% of insurance sector executives surveyed felt highly prepared for disruptive innovation over the five-year horizon.[21] Now, the virus has hit the insurance industry like an extinction level event and huge losses are anticipated across the sector well beyond the pandemic. Insurers no longer have the luxury of time to make meaningful changes to their purpose, people, and processes. Plans must be formulated and enacted soon if incumbents are to survive the ongoing disruption and immediate aftermath of the crisis and thrive in the post-pandemic era.

Risk Attitudes

The US and Eurozone's economies could take until 2023 or beyond to fully recover from the impact of the pandemic crisis, while the industries hardest hit, including insurance, may see an even slower recovery. Attitudes to risk, particularly within supply chains, are likely to shift quite suddenly. Indeed, lasting change to supply chains is possible should the virus become seasonal, endemic, or evolve variants for which there is no effective vaccine or treatment. Changes could be profound, given the interrelated weight of risk that was beginning to impact the world pre-pandemic, namely an unstable geopolitical environment, climate change, and the emergence of regionalization over globalization.

Insurance Journal estimates that 75% of IT spending in the insurance industry is on maintaining legacy systems, but technology innovation stands to transform the nature of risk and the business of insurance by 2030.[22] Indeed, it is technology, and new technologies in particular, that will enable insurers to adapt products and services, better monitor client risk, get a stronger handle on their data, and ultimately facilitate future investments.

The InsurTech Opportunity

The longer-term impact of the crisis and the rise of InsurTech may be to drive a wave of digitalization and innovation in the industry, as market conditions mitigate against the continuation of incremental change and "business as usual" thinking. In February 2020, prior to the potential impacts of the pandemic being fully understood, it had been forecast by Insurance Thought Leadership that InsurTech funding up to 2025 would be greater than the prior ten years combined.[23] The depth and length of the crisis may well impact the viability of many

InsurTechs, perhaps lending insurers the upper hand in acquiring new ideas and innovation cheaply. Some distress is already evident, with several InsurTechs reducing headcounts.

InsurTechs offer a way of infusing new ideas, technologies, and applications into the industry and ultimately creating the potential for building innovative service propositions. Globally, Accenture estimates that insurers who transform their businesses and operating models could see US$375 billion in new revenue growth, but highlights that InsurTechs are often quicker to craft new services in this changed environment.[24]

The way technology is being adopted across society could also have a profound impact on the sector. People, sensors, and devices are increasingly becoming interconnected in an Internet of Things (IoT). This is a development which, in many cases, takes the notion of insurance way beyond the sector's normal operating models and practices, requiring agility, new skills, and access to alternative data sources. The effects are already being felt, with Accenture also finding 96% of insurers acknowledging the impact of digital ecosystems on their industry.

Changing Models

Raconteur research from 2020 finds that some 89% of insurers expect that, within five years, personalized insurance will be expected as a standard practice.[25] This will require greater levels of trust, real-time data analytics capabilities, and an organization structure able to respond in real time. All of these developments will further evolve the role of insurance from compensators to preventers of loss. This goal will take a renewed commitment to digital transformation, not just for the life of the pandemic, but for the period afterwards.

Within just a few years, most new business systems will incorporate real-time contextual data which will lead to improved business decisions. This innovation and better use of data, derived from the IoT, will enable personalized, real-time products and services and the ability to tap into ad hoc markets. This demands concurrent shifts in insurance processes: witness, for example, that the predicted value of artificial intelligence (AI) underwritten insurance premiums alone could exceed US$20 billion by 2024, from US$1.3 billion in 2019.[26] Generally, AI could both streamline current processes and create new revenue pools.

Tomorrow's Ecosystems

The harsh business and economic environments are likely to persist for longer than the acute phase of the pandemic health crisis, meaning that enhancing productivity must now assume a central role for all insurers. This means access to reliable, comprehensive, and timely data and the ecosystems that enable it.

For insurers, it will become essential to tap into an ecosystem that offers the opportunity to embed their products into customer journeys seamlessly. Already, most incumbents are involved with at least one partnership ecosystem. In this new operating environment, they have found that being easy to partner with from a technological perspective has become a critical aspect of their strategy.

CapGemini's 2020 research found that, despite insurers' wishes for more collaboration, just 11% leverage an open architecture required for collaboration and only 32% collaborate with the ecosystem to provide value-added services.[27] Some insurers have already created their own ecosystem which is proving to be a significant channel to market.

How Can Insurers go Forward?

In the short term, a reputation of trustworthiness earned through the crisis could shape an insurer's image for decades. It will prove essential to change for greater flexibility, adopt new processes, and pivot toward greater investment in digital capabilities and the people and skills to use them effectively. In order to be better prepared for ongoing volatility and disruptive change, the use of methods such as scenario planning will become accepted as a vital strategic tool.

In the mid-term (one to three years), it becomes essential to elevate strategic partnerships and broader collaboration. As the data from new technologies assumes a more important element of business processes and propositions, it will be key to monitor how big tech companies are using it and identify how end consumers can benefit from the data held about them. At the same time, it will be essential to identify and develop leadership that can take the organization from the current digital era into the intelligent era.

For the long term (three years+), insurers must prepare for public–private partnerships since insuring pandemics and other meta-scale events may prove too vast a risk for insurers to handle alone. There will be a need to adapt traditional siloed, line-of-business, pooled insurance products into customer-centric, personalized propositions. Ultimately, a core competence of the industry will be the ability to become even more data-driven through partnerships, ecosystems, and the creation of new revenue streams.

- *In what way could we use new technologies to improve productivity and drive innovation?*
- *What might our new propositions look like as a consequence of employing technology innovation?*
- *What new skills and job roles do we envisage we will need to be successful in an increasingly digitized world?*

David Smith is the chief executive and a futurist at Global Futures and Foresight, a futures research firm, based in London. He has over 35 years of technology, marketing, leadership, and strategy experience. He is a keynote speaker at conferences and regularly publishes forward-looking insights reports.

Collectively Producing Zero-Waste Food: Zainab's Scenario in 2025

By Dr. Nisreen Lahham

How might we ensure food security in 2025 in light of the pandemic's impacts on the food supply chain?

This chapter uses scenario thinking to explore the possible implications of the pandemic on our future food security. The analysis examines the issue of food security in light of restricted food imports and disconnected supply chains. The chapter concludes by discussing the responses we could make to these challenges and examines how they could shape a revolutionary new scenario for the agricultural sector.

Standing outside her farm on June 30th, 2025, Zainab, a 34-year-old Egyptian farm owner, is reminiscing about her life in 2020, during the early days of the pandemic. She remembered a time when borders were sealed off, and travel, imports, and exports were restricted. Food supply chains from rural areas to cities were disconnected and food prices were increasing. Water scarcity and the adverse impacts of climate change restricted national agricultural development, so Egypt, being reliant then on wheat and cereal imports, was vulnerable to these supply shocks and international price volatility.

Zainab recalled the day she decided to return to her small village, quitting her job as a government employee and leaving Cairo, to run her own sugarcane farming business. Her decision was driven by the newly ignited appreciation and demand for farming as a profession, after decades of farmers leaving the sector and migrating to Cairo and other big cities. This new appreciation of farming was a direct result of glocalization, and the governmental policy move to secure food domestically, in response to the threat of the pandemic.

Over the last five years, the Egyptian government had responded to the food crisis by trying to maximize domestic food production, with a shift toward supporting local small-scale farmers and creating a more sustainable food system. This entailed developing practices through agricultural research institutions, which became application-focused, demonstrative, and educational.

Now, in 2025, these institutions are highly equipped to develop new species of plants that can tolerate high temperatures while requiring minimal amounts of water. This was essential in applying the policy of securing food domestically in a predominantly arid environment. Moreover, leveraging Fourth Industrial Revolution technology tools allowed for the widespread adoption of data-driven precision agriculture, which vastly reduced the level of inputs required to grow crops, as each plant got just what it needed.

The reformed agricultural research institutions also allow Zainab and her peers to expand their agricultural knowledge, connecting them and providing access to information on new technologies and agricultural practices. These advances were accompanied by governmental support to farmers to fulfill their learning ambitions. After initially being perceived largely as knowledge recipients, farmers are now encouraged to share their acquired expertise and contribute to research in order to further drive the advancement of national agricultural practices. The participatory agricultural research between farmers and academia is a good example of the increased value placed by the government on farmers' knowledge and experience.

Like other farmers, Zainab is seeking out new horizons to expand her sugarcane farming business. She and her peers are incentivized to combine farming with agri-business. In the world of 2025, the business of agriculture is a generalized occupation: "Every farmer is a businessperson." Farmers now manufacture food products in addition to planting agricultural crops. The private sector works with research institutions and farmers as well, acting as an intermediary between knowledge providers and practitioners.

Green technology and businesses are equally valued and create new business and career opportunities. The government incentivizes eco-digital farms which create an auto-sufficient environment, with minimal usage of water and energy. Soil-enhancing fertilizers help in maximizing food production, while also combating the challenges presented by the harsh climatic conditions. Moreover, the food products of these eco-digital farms are marketed directly to consumers through digital platforms connecting small farmers with consumers all over Egypt.

Zainab had decided to produce sugar from sugarcane, after coming across the idea on social media. She asked her associate Sara, who owns a small intermediary enterprise, to develop a business plan for a sugarcane factory that encompasses an environment-friendly nexus approach. This approach is designed to increase water, energy, and food security by encouraging those working in one sector to be mindful of their impact on other adjacent sectors.

In addition to sugar production, Sara suggested using sugarcane residue, known as bagasse, for generating power to run the factory. She also proposed using the excess power generated to supplement the solar powered irrigation systems deployed on her farm, and to supply electricity to her house. Zainab now plans to use the remaining waste as animal feed and for producing molasses, which could be used for ethyl alcohol production, for which demand has been growing post-pandemic.

Despite at first not having sufficient capital to implement her business idea, newly established financial schemes allowed Zainab to gain access to bank loans through intermediary companies. These advisors develop feasibility studies and facilitate access to finance for farmers. The required financing for this envisioned sugarcane factory could also have come in the form of aid provided by the agricultural development bank in her village, which supports small farming enterprises. Additionally, government incentives for farmers such as tax exemptions and Green Bonds have been made available to boost the green agricultural business sector.

Governmental incentives don't target farmers exclusively. Any person can benefit from food production incentives. A new "do it yourself" system allows consumers to become food producers. In 2025, members of the public are encouraged to grow their own food—for example using aquaponic systems that allow the growing of plants without soil, by using mineral nutrient solutions in a water solvent. These systems are now available on the market at reasonable prices.

Aquaponic installations are highly subsidized by the government, as they consume 70% less water than conventional farming methods. Simple agricultural toolkits are available to individuals interested in practicing farming to secure their own food supply, with the possibility of selling excess food to local markets. In addition, as a central part of the education curriculum, each school is equipped with a garden to produce and sell food.

As Zainab was waiting for Sara, she glanced at her emerald green farm, witnessing her crops being packaged by automated machines. She remembered the days in early 2020, when the pandemic first hit the world, feeling grateful for the great awakening it created. It motivated the government to make the bold decision to develop and implement a revolutionary vision for securing national food supplies.

The vision required a paradigm shift in the agricultural sector. The walls that once separated farmers, the private sector, research institutions, and the public have been torn down. Interdisciplinary knowledge has gained increased attention. Modern empirical science and technological know-how are transferred to farmers. These fundamental shifts allowed farmers, researchers, and citizens to independently secure national and individual food supplies. As a result of this paradigm shift, Zainab's village has been recognized worldwide as self-sufficient, using modern technology to produce organic food with zero waste.

- *What implications might the pandemic have for future food security?*
- *What actions can we take to ensure food security in light of restricted imports and disconnected supply chains?*
- *How might innovative science and technology based responses shape a new revolutionary scenario for agricultural sector businesses in both the developing and developed world?*

Dr. Nisreen Lahham is a regional project manager for Wastewater Reuse in the MENA Region at the International Water Management Institute (IWMI). She is the founder and head of the Future Studies Forum for Africa and the Middle East and was the executive manager of the Center for Future Studies at the Egyptian Cabinet's Information and Decision Support Center.

Five Technologies Shaping the Post-Pandemic Future of Food

By Tony Hunter

What do global pandemics reveal to us about the opportunities and vulnerabilities of our global food system that could be addressed through key technological advances?

The 2020-21 pandemic has irrevocably changed our world. But what could the legacy of the pandemic be for the very future of the food, beverage, and agri-food industries? Has it fundamentally changed the trajectory of these industries?

There are many developments shaping the future of food, ranging from natural farming approaches, advances in agricultural science, and precision agriculture, through to technology developments, better use of data analytics, and innovations in food processing. However, in this chapter, I want to focus in on the future potential of five critical and exponentially advancing technologies that were already exerting a growing influence on the future of food pre-pandemic.

The five key technologies I want to discuss are genomics, the microbiome, cellular agriculture, alternative proteins, and synthetic biology. These could have an even greater impact in the coming years as we seek to tackle issues and risks made starkly apparent during the crisis. These include hunger and food security, food sovereignty, cost, waste, supply chain vulnerabilities, quality, reliability, environmental impacts, and sustainability. So, the legitimate question arises as to what were the knock-on effects of the pandemic on these technologies in relation to the future of food?

Looking at the recent signals of change in these technologies suggests that their development continues and that they are still central to the future food agenda. In practice, product sales are surging for alternative proteins and microbiome-based gut health solutions; genomics and synthetic biology are being combined to fight the virus and generate valuable new insights; the cellular agriculture research agenda has been largely unaffected; and venture capital investment in "agri-foodtech" continues largely unabated. Hence, from these and other signals, we can be confident that these technologies remain relevant and that developments may actually be accelerating in the face of the current pandemic.

Despite the continuing disruption, these signals suggest that the fundamental long-term trajectory for the use of these technologies in the food, beverage, and agri-food industries remains unchanged or has in some cases been accelerated. So, as the world seeks to recover from the pandemic and stabilize food supplies, let's explore the potential development paths of these emerging technology fields and possible industry impacts over the two- to five-year time frame.

When looking at the two- to five-year horizon, the major lesson for food manufacturers to learn from the current crisis is the extreme vulnerability of currently high labor industries during a microbial pandemic. We've seen the conventional meat sector close entire facto- ries in the US and Europe, potentially causing major protein shortages. Thousands of tons of vegetables around the world have been plowed back into the soil or left to rot due to a lack of labor, a situation exac- erbated by falling demand due to restaurant closures.

In the dairy sector, milk was poured down the drain as conventional industries with long lead times and little control on supply were unable to react quickly to market changes. Hence, automation across the food supply chain, which may have seemed too expensive in 2019, may increasingly look like a good idea in 2022 and beyond.

Our local and global food systems have been exposed as working well only when there is relative stability of supply and demand, and each element performs perfectly. The problem is a lack of resilience in times of crisis. Equally importantly, the negative implications of the globalization of the food supply chain are now becoming obvious. These vulnerabilities include susceptibility to transport disruptions, and a lack of labor to pick, process, and manufacture basic foods. Additionally, some countries temporarily banned the export of staples like wheat, soybeans, flour, sugar, and potatoes. Hence, the perceived advantage of many of the five technologies above is that they do not suffer from these constraints and are far more agile in adapting to short lead time changes.

Food production has long been tied to the availability of arable land and fresh water. Those countries that have them have food security; those that don't are at the mercy of those that do. These and other factors have dramatic implications for the short- and long-term food sovereignty of many countries and the global, equitable distribution of food.

De-coupling food from this tyranny of arable land and available water would enable many countries to avoid supply issues and attain a high level of self-sufficiency and food security. Until recently, this has been an impossibility; however, technologies such as those discussed here can now change this seemingly fundamental basis of food production. The technologists' argument is that developing and even developed countries have no need to continue to pursue only conventional technologies.

The hope is that we can increasingly isolate our food supply from the transborder impacts of pandemics and reimagine our food system to use non-arable land and even salt water to produce food and food ingredients. By pursuing a portfolio of developments drawn from these five core technologies such as cultivated meat, algae, and synthetic biology, countries can establish a whole new food system and achieve greater individual food self-sufficiency and security.

For some time, we have seen players in the food sector making great efforts to persuade us that we can feed the future global population properly. Their strategy is one of equitably distributing food products from one part of the globe to another to take advantage of scale efficiencies. The fallacy of this approach has been exposed by the pandemic. In times of extreme crisis, food rich countries have reserved products for themselves, and the usual recipients of their exported food products suffer.

In my view, the answer to feeding the global population will not be in the equitable distribution of food but in the equitable distribution of food production technologies. While this may result in a more siloed system, it should prove to be a much more resilient one. The promise of such an approach is that over a two- to five-year period, countries could become increasingly self-sufficient in at least basic nutrition, making them far less susceptible to food shortages in a crisis, even if it doesn't all taste good.

Pausing to look beyond our pandemic imposed isolation, there is a clear imperative to take the time to review the very foundations and functioning of our food system. To return to business as usual would be a waste of a crisis. This review is particularly important as it's a matter of when, not if, another microbial pandemic occurs, and how companies and countries plan for this inevitability is critical.

Given the current pandemic's massive impact on the world, how do we develop a plan for the unfolding, but somewhat unknowable, future? Simply dusting off the one-, three-, or five-year pre-pandemic plan and starting where we left off just won't cut it or tackle the range of issues discussed here. To do so is simply returning to a tired old linear thinking approach. Furthermore, if there's one thing the current pandemic has demonstrated clearly, it's the danger of restrictive linear thinking in an exponential world.

Our perspectives have been challenged in the most extreme ways possible and we need to completely reimagine the possible futures of food using strategic foresight. I would argue that the foresight approach needs to be driven from a basis of what technology could enable, since they shape consumer needs as much as consumer needs shape technologies. Using this framing, we can plan for many possible futures and give ourselves the agility and adaptability needed to respond to a range of possible futures in the years to come.

I believe there is a massive range of food supply chain transformation opportunities presented by these technologies. The payoff will be maximized by those companies and countries that can both adapt where necessary to cope with the short-term impacts of the pandemic, while also preparing and planning for the longer term using strategic foresight.

Will the legacy of the pandemic be simply the human toll, or will it be the inflection point for a whole new way of thinking about the global food system? There are many possible post-pandemic futures for the global food system, and which one becomes reality will be our choice.

- *How can we enable developing countries to skip conventional food production processes and technologies as many did with telephone communications?*
- *How can we re-engineer the global food system to increase local resilience and better cope with pandemics?*
- *What are the possible futures of food as critical technologies reach exponential tipping points?*

Tony Hunter is a global futurist, speaker, and foresight strategy consultant specializing in the future of food. He uses signals provided by emerging technologies to explore the agri-food industry's long-term future over the next 10+ years.

Post-Pandemic Urban Mobility: A Tale of Three Regions

By Boyd Cohen

The trillion-dollar question for the global mobility ecosystem is what regulatory, economic, and behavioral changes might we see when we have passed the pandemic?

The pandemic has had an impact on every aspect of life in cities. The mobility sector has been one of the hardest hit. During the earliest stages of lockdowns, in some markets in North America and Europe, public transit use declined up to 80% and several ride hailing and micro mobility operators reduced or even ceased operations. In many locations, passenger vehicle use fell precipitously during the crisis and may not recover fully.

These dramatic impacts on mobility in communities around the globe arose as regional and national governments sought to confine people to their homes. The goal was to increase social distancing and thus drive down the transmission of the virus. In parallel, many cities took the opportunity to either accelerate measures to further restrict car use or tentatively explore new traffic curbing measures. Streets have been converted to pedestrian areas and cycling paths to allow for increased social distancing. This has allowed greater freedom of personal movement to citizens in quarantine areas.

Existing trends, and the attitudes and orientations of different regions toward mobility, had been on very different trajectories well before the crisis, and now these potentially more permanent post-pandemic changes are taking place. Hence, in the developed world, as these forces combine, we could see different possible post-pandemic urban mobility paths emerge in North America, Europe, and Asian cities. Across these regions, we have witnessed widely differing views on personal car ownership, the use of transport technology, and the role of public transit. Post-pandemic, these differences could accelerate the growing variations in approaches to personal and collective mobility.

Post-Pandemic North America: The Car is Still King!

The US, having seen rapid expansion of its cities after World War Two (WWII), has had a love affair with the autonomy and freedom of the personal car. The advent of the automobile for the masses contributed to the explosion of suburbs and multi-car households. While there is some evidence suggesting growing rates of urban migration in the US, the role of the car in urban and suburban life has never been stronger. In fact, even before the pandemic, public transit use in the US was in decline. During the pandemic, usage has declined even more precipitously, leaving public transit authorities (PTAs) around the country suffering the consequences.

The US commitment to investment in public transit and rail infrastructure has always been weak, so the PTAs were already at a competitive disadvantage to those in Europe and Asia. Americans who can afford to own and operate their own vehicle are more likely than ever to embrace the private automobile post-pandemic. They now have yet one more reason to avoid public transit—a greater sense of control and safety. Those who don't or can't own a car must rely on public transport.

As transit authorities are forced to cut back services, those lucky enough to have a job are finding fewer options available to get to work. We will likely continue to see growing privatization of transit services, including further expansion of demand responsive transit (DRT) as a more cost-effective, yet controversial alternative to fixed route transit services.

Pre-pandemic, the US was already leading the effort to embrace autonomous personal vehicle technology development and deployment. In the next five years, we are likely to see continued investment and larger scale trials of private driverless vehicles and autonomous ride hailing initiatives like those from Uber and Google. An acceleration of interest in autonomous personal vehicles will likely arise as Americans retrench to their preferred form of mobility, the private automobile. While some cities in Canada like Vancouver, Montreal, and Toronto have a stronger focus on public transit and micro mobility than their southern neighbors, much of Canada could follow a similar trajectory to the US.

It is not all doom and gloom in the US. The Biden administration has placed renewed emphasis on infrastructure including an ambitious transportation revitalization plan that would involve spending US$85 billion to modernize the transit system across the country. This includes interest in rethinking the role of passenger rail as a low-carbon alternative to moving large numbers of people through Amtrak but also private rail operators such as Brightline Trains.

Post-Pandemic Europe: MaaS, Micro Mobility, and Social Distancing

Many European cities, established centuries before the automobile, have a robust system of rail and public transit connections. After WWII, several important European automobile manufacturers emerged and some markets like Germany embraced the private automobile almost as much as America. Yet mass transit, rail, and micro mobility (starting with personal bike use and evolving to include bike sharing) have remained prevalent throughout the region. Before the pandemic, there was growing momentum around two related topics: 1) reducing carbon emissions from transit by further supporting a modal shift away from cars and planes and toward more sustainable solutions like rail and micro mobility; and 2) the idea of Mobility as a Service (MaaS).

Mobility as a Service is the concept of offering residents and visitors to a city or region a single interface to access a range of public and private mobility services including rail, metro, bus, taxis, ride hailing, and micro mobility. In Europe in particular, the MaaS movement arose out of the growing fragmentation of the mobility ecosystem. For example, some cities have 60 or more private mobility services, each with their own apps competing for users' attention. While definitions vary, MaaS platforms aspire to enable users to find the best routes to go from A to B, including combining public and private mobility services, and to book and pay for those services inside one app.

Mobility as a Service has become a big industry in Europe, represented by the MaaS Alliance and several homegrown European and UK based players like Citymapper, MaaS Global (Whim), and Iomob. Prior to the pandemic, Europe was the hotbed for micro mobility operators. There were three dozen regional players actively offering sharing services for bikes, kick scooters, and mopeds. During the crisis, many of these players had to shut down entirely or pivot to some other use for their shared vehicles. Quarantined Europeans were either not going out or avoiding shared vehicles to prevent contact with potentially infected surfaces.

Some micro mobility operators will not survive, but those that do will likely enhance their service with measures such as self-cleaning handlebars and disinfecting kits for users. Meanwhile, MaaS platforms should embrace the incorporation of social distancing factors into their routing algorithms to allow people additional peace of mind with suitably designed routing options.

Ultimately, the pandemic may also accelerate the shift away from cars and toward human-centered urban infrastructure that was already underway. Increasing amounts of public space and urban roads are likely to be converted to dedicated spaces for pedestrians, supporting both motorized and non-motorized micro mobility while diverting roads previously allocated to private cars. The UK alone announced a £2 billion fund to support the growth of active travel corridors in cities throughout the country.

Post-Pandemic Asia: Tech-Driven, Safer, but Invasive Mass Transit

Many Asian cities are massive in terms of their physical scale and population size. In response to these drivers, those cities that can afford it will likely continue to invest in mass transit and high-speed rail infrastructure. Asian cities were among the first to embrace new smart city technologies. As we have seen during the pandemic, they have also been bolstered by more centralized decision-making and planning at the federal government level. This has enabled them to incorporate citizen tracing features to track infected or exposed users in transit, whether that be the mass use of facial recognition, or mechanisms to trace infected citizens' movements.

Many Asian nations and cities appear to be on the path toward a technology-centered, mass surveillance driven, mobility management model. Some experts such as Yuval Harari have warned us about the risks to society if a "Surveillance Economy" were to emerge. My expectation is that we will see an expansion of citizen surveillance while in transit across many Asian nations. This will be coupled with continued investment in mass transit as the only viable way to move so many people efficiently on a daily basis.

Conclusion

It is impossible to paint all cities and regions with one mobility strategy brush. That is certainly true with respect to how our mobility patterns will be affected by decisions we make as residents and the paths our governments take as they try to plan their way out of the pandemic. In a recent post on the Financial Times blog, Harari suggested that some governments will take this opportunity to impose "temporary" surveillance solutions that will become institutionalized after the pandemic. I believe that outcome could become prevalent in several Asian cities.

In the US, it seems we may witness a "back to the future" retrenchment to the personal automobile with growing adoption of autonomous vehicles. Meanwhile in Europe, expect further use of safer forms of intermodal journeys enabled by MaaS platforms. This will likely be coupled with some new and existing micro mobility operators embracing social distancing and new technologies to make shared mobility safer.

- *Can anything break the declining investment in, and utilization of, public transit in many cities around the world?*
- *Can Mobility as a Service usher in a wave of low-carbon mobility in Europe and beyond?*
- *How might developing countries adapt their mobility strategies for a post-pandemic world?*

Boyd Cohen, Ph.D., is the co-founder and CEO of Iomob, building a global plug and play mobility on demand platform. He has published three books on sustainable entrepreneurship and urban innovation. Boyd has been a keynote and TEDx speaker, Fast Company contributor, and consultant on smart cities and sustainable mobility for more than a decade.

The Reinvention of Travel— and Residency

By Hjörtur Smárason

How Might the Travel Sector Evolve and would now be a good time to start a new electric airline?

Tourism is the world's third largest export economy, and one of the fastest growing industries, with women representing over 54% of employees. The pandemic saw the sector plunged into crisis, with a 70% decrease in tourism worldwide, and 100% of global destinations implementing travel restrictions at some point in 2020.

While tourism in general is expected to recover by 2024 or 2025, many in the sector fear it may never return to the same patterns as before. The tourism sector that rises from the ashes could be very different with changed demand patterns, behaviors, and products, although I wouldn't hold my breath about the prospects for sectoral growth until truly commercially viable electric airlines emerge and spread their wings.

Reopening Restrictions
To start with, we are seeing regional openings and travel being allowed in bubbles such as within China and the European Union (EU). With limited vaccination roll-outs in many developing countries, we can

expect to see continued travel restrictions in those markets, which creates interesting second order impacts. Firstly, it curbs the impact of tourism as a force of economic development where it is most needed. Secondly, it encourages domestic and intraregional travel.

Destinations you can reach by car or train are already seeing increased popularity in many countries, while long-haul travel could struggle even more and for an extended period. The economic consequences could therefore be felt much harder outside of the main travel markets, of China, the EU, and the US respectively. Surveys among travelers in the UK, EU, and US show that domestic travel is on a sharp rise with rural and nature breaks topping the destination wish list. Alaska is trending strongly in the US, while a cabin holiday in the Lake District or Wales is the rising trend in the UK.

Emerging Travel Priorities—Multimodal, Familiarity, and Safety

Post-pandemic travel behaviors are likely to be driven by governmental restrictions, and changes in demand. There is likely to be growing need for certainty in uncertain times. With the volatility around travel expected to continue for some time, people can be expected to look for ways to mitigate the risks. Familiarity plays a big role in one's sense of security. The default is that the unknown is the unsafe.

Destinations people have been to previously seem likely to become more attractive because travelers know what to expect there. The same goes for destinations where people speak your language or share your culture. Even though it might be a new destination, the common understanding created through language or culture means that travelers could feel they know more about what to expect. But there are also other ways in which demand is likely to continue changing.

Our chosen mode of transport is already seeing significant shifts as a result of limitations on air and sea travel. The trend toward self-drive holidays and the use of rail are likely to keep rising, with destinations within shorter distances becoming ever more attractive. The choice of type of destination is also changing. People are looking for getaways that are stress-free, and more importantly, crowd-free. The popularity of rural destinations can be expected to continue seeing sharp rises, along with options such as nature-based vacations, farm stays, cabin breaks, and hiking holidays.

In the shorter term, while the opportunity for international travel remains uncertain, the quick city break to the classic destinations such as Rome, Paris, Amsterdam, or London are likely to suffer. On the other hand, the situation might open up opportunities for easily accessible secondary cities to come onto the scene more strongly as destinations, offering some of the same experiences as bigger cities but without the large crowds and perceived higher risks.

Destinations will need to think about these changing demand influences and behaviors in their communication strategies. How are they mitigating the risks? How are they making sure sanitary standards are being maintained and communicated as a traveler safety priority? As demand rises, they will also need to make sure that vehicle-based tourists do not experience traffic bottlenecks and delays, with the resulting risk of being stuck in a small space with too many individuals.

Technology could play a big role in the future of tourism. Not only could it lower operating costs and financial risks for operators, it could also become instrumental in attracting tourist flows, avoiding clustering, and, maybe most importantly, delivering a touchless tourism experience. Touchless booking processes, check-in procedures, and door handles could become as common as the touchless bathroom faucet has become today.

Rethinking the Business of Travel

In the business-to-business market, commercial tourism is likely to undergo further deep and rapid changes. Virtual communication has proven itself to be a viable alternative for a lot of business travel. There currently seems little chance that all of the routes flown in 2019 will open up again soon, or perhaps ever. The least popular and less profitable business and leisure routes could continue to be scrapped and airlines will increasingly be on the lookout for new routes tied to changes in the attractiveness of different geographic markets.

For business customers, leisure travelers, and airlines alike, the distances between originating locations and target markets, and the associated flight costs, could have a big impact on decision-making. For airlines, the expectations of demand growth and financial incentives from destinations will be key determinants of the profitability of every route under consideration.

Destination branding and the product portfolio offered could also rise in importance. Travel agents and wholesalers will also need to rethink their offerings, pricing, and support services in order to attract the more profitable business traveler alongside the leisure market. They too will be looking for new products that meet changing patterns and types of demand.

A key sectoral challenge will be to manage the distribution of lower levels of demand across an increasingly wide range of options encompassing more rural retreats, nature-based vacations, different kinds of city escape, closer-by options, longer duration breaks, and more sustainable destinations. In the face of this fast-changing demand landscape, those destinations that fail to adapt to a new reality and new demand could suffer, while the popularity of unexpected destinations could be on the rise.

Travel with Purpose

Generational differences are becoming increasingly important across every consumer-facing market. In many countries, millennials are rejecting the notion of a regular "nine to five" job. In the US for example, for many the "American Dream" of working and putting in the hours to buy a suburban home and a station wagon has lost its appeal.

There is a growing sense globally that millennials want a job with a purpose. Attitudes to travel could be no different. Even before the pandemic, we were already hearing about "flight shaming" because of the environmental impact of air travel. It was already a big thing in Sweden, the homeland of environmental activist Greta Thunberg, and on the rise across the western hemisphere.

Alongside the environmental concerns, we now also need to think about pandemics and the risks of catching or transmitting a virus when traveling. For many millennials in particular, justification of travel modes is becoming an increasing issue; you don't just jump on a plane for fun. You need to have a purpose. Are you flying to do something in particular, meet someone, reunite with friends or family, participate in a learning experience, or contribute your time to something of value to society?

Travel product development could increasingly be shaped by the need for purpose. How can we attract the "contributing traveler"? How can we cater for those seeking a responsible tourism experience which minimizes their impact on the environment and local society? How should we focus on and communicate the positive impact the traveler can have?

There are two dimensions of purpose to consider. Firstly, how can the traveler contribute to their own development, whether professional or personal, through courses, workshops, training, and education of all sorts? Secondly, how can the traveler contribute to, or participate in, activities that support the preservation, sustainability, and development of the location?

Traveler contributions could be as simple as beach cleaning and picking strawberries. At a higher level, the traveler could provide access to their expertise, perspectives, and networks. Over time, the notion of travel could increasingly broaden out from the simple notion of a holiday breaking away from the daily nine-to-five routine. We are starting to see travel as an individual and societal enrichment activity with a higher purpose and a slower pace.

The Future of Work and Reversal of the Brain Drain

Working from home proved easier than we thought, and maybe one of the best long-term outcomes of the crisis could be a permanent reduction of commuting by over 20%, with a consequent decrease in pollution. This could be achieved through people working from home, or at a local co-working space, for one day a week on average. Working at an office and "on the clock" could become so last century. The same goes for business travel. While still essential in some circumstances, it could decrease considerably, especially when it comes to conferences and events. Many of those are now run online with higher participation enabling increased sharing of information and greater international cooperation. Many events could continue in this way or evolve into hybrid experiences.

After the lockdowns, living in the countryside could continue to be more attractive and much more doable with the acceptance of remote working. Even traditional boutique shops should have a better chance of surviving by operating from anywhere thanks to online shopping becoming more the norm. The brain drain from many countries has also been temporarily reversed, and some may choose to stay in their home country while working remotely for an employer on the other side of the world.

The rise of rural living could be further empowered by a growth in local co-working spaces, and driven by individuals' increased demand for personal space. At present, it feels like we could never go back to our previous behaviors as office rats doing in-store shopping. For many, the nine-to-five commute has already become a faded memory, replaced by fresh air, a broadband connection, or satellite linked computer, and abundant personal space. This shift could impact both travel and residency in general.

Digital Nomads and the Future of Residency

One of the more interesting challenges we could see is the emergence of the digital nomad. Not that it hasn't been a concept for quite a while, but now we could be seeing an exponential growth where more and more people are spending two, three, and up to six months on the road, or in different locations. This could open up a new genre of slow travelers, the workcation nomads. At the same time, it could be challenging when it comes to taxes and the services taxes we pay for such things as children's education, healthcare, and social services.

Interestingly, in the digital era, what is there to say a city has to be limited to its geographical area? Perhaps one future lies in the form of a fluid city where you sign up to a system like you sign up to a pension fund or an insurance program today. You decide where you are a citizen, but you do not necessarily live there. Estonia has already laid the groundwork with its e-residency program. Your city could be your clan, your place brand identity, social security program, online medical consulting, and education system, but not your location.

Living in the clouds could take on a whole new meaning.

- *Tourism could recover, but in what shape and form?*
- *What could be the main drivers of tourism demand in the post-pandemic world?*
- *How might the notion of residency evolve and what forms could it take in the future?*

Hjörtur Smárason is the CEO of Visit Greenland and is leading the restart of tourism in the country. He has worked on place branding, tourism development, and crisis communications strategies for cities, regions, and countries in Africa, Asia, and Europe.

Post-Pandemic Public Education: Four Scenarios for the United States

By Jason Siko

How might the post-pandemic economic recovery and possible shifts in the political landscape shape the future of US public education?

This chapter explores four possible 2025 scenarios for public education in the US. One major disruption during the pandemic was the closure of buildings for K-12 schools serving the 5–17 age group. Affluent districts made a quick conversion to remote online learning, while others could only send home packets of paper worksheets on the last day of normal schooling. The pandemic highlighted not only how socio-economic factors affect access to healthcare, but also how they impact access to quality education. Aside from educating children, public education is "very affordable daycare" for working parents, and many children rely heavily on schools for their nutritional needs.

Alongside the pandemic, US schools had experienced a variety of disruptive events over the previous 20 years. These included 9/11, numerous natural disasters, and too many school shootings to count. The fact that many districts had no continuity-of-learning plan in place for a situation like the 2020 pandemic was appalling, but not shocking.

Furthermore, public opinion of K-12 schools had wavered over several decades and become heavily politicized, with considerable debate over issues related to funding, accountability, and market-driven reforms.

Opinions on how schools handled the pandemic can shift or reinforce these sentiments, often based on political allegiances. The speed of a post-pandemic economic recovery will influence schools over the next five years. Without greater funding financed through tax revenues, the inequities brought to light may only be exacerbated. The pace of the economic recovery, along with shifting public attitudes, make up the axes for developing four scenarios describing how public education might be faring in 2025: Kill Your Heroes, Mothers of Invention, Jack Be Nimble, and React and Return.

Kill Your Heroes (Slow Recovery, Negative Attitude)

After the first week of school closures in 2020, parents lamented on social media that teachers should be paid much more. After the pandemic subsided and economic realities set in, this novel idea faded quickly. Over the period to 2025, school funding was slashed, and teachers endured further cuts to salaries and benefits. Since few would take on enormous student loan debt in return for a teacher's starting salary, staff shortages became evident everywhere. This drove a relaxation of requirements and allowed less well trained and lower skilled adults to become teachers. Not surprisingly, quality suffered, but fitted the plans of market-driven reformers.

Players in the for-profit education sector were quick to capitalize on this shift, building remote teaching infrastructure, which included multiple ways to harvest student data. Greater use was also made of more adaptive learning platforms, driven by artificial intelligence (AI), and monitored by para-professional staff. While many parents were unhappy with remote teaching during the pandemic, these improvements drove more parents to choose this option. This trend was reinforced by fears stoked by evangelical and conservative groups during the pandemic about being in proximity to "other" people.

Mothers of Invention (Slow Recovery, Positive Attitude)

An unintended consequence of the pandemic was a disruption in standardized testing. The 2020 election brought in a more progressive agenda, and the federal government relaxed testing and accountability requirements for several years as a result. Teachers were given the gift of freedom to teach in the way that they felt would be most beneficial to their students. Initial school closures again resulted in social media protests by parents, but five years on, school funding and teacher salaries and benefits have been cut. Less qualified teachers fill many staffing gaps and the lament about the impact on the quality of education largely goes unheeded.

However, the pandemic brought to light the creative and resourceful mindset of educators, who were asked to radically change their teaching methods almost overnight. Encouraged to educate "by any means necessary," teachers explored innovative ways to deliver student learning experiences, creating a new "golden age" of learning that echoed Dewey and other progressive educators.

Over the next few years, flexible open educational resources, maker spaces, and service learning (combining community service with educational objectives) dominated K-12 classrooms. There was also an emphasis on the trades and civic participation. While some of these programs proved expensive to run, local districts relied heavily on the charity and participation of community members, along with public–private partnerships with local businesses.

Jack Be Nimble (Quick Recovery, Positive Attitude)

The economic recovery from the pandemic was swift, and attitudes toward education were favorable for making changes. Infrastructure and stimulus plans dedicated resources to districts to eliminate barriers to access in impoverished communities, including supplying families with laptops and improving Internet access.

Part of the infrastructure plan included a requirement that school districts develop continuity plans that detail how schools handle closures in the future. With the 2020 virus returning the following winter, these went beyond exhaustive pandemic planning to cater for a wider range of disruptions due to weather, earthquakes, terrorism, and climate change.

An unintended consequence of these changes was a major shift in schools toward competency-based grading and Universal Design for Learning—a modern approach to teaching, learning, and curriculum design that accounts for atypical neurological types. Learning continues regardless of the situation, and curricula are designed to be flexible, offering multiple paths for learning and demonstrating competency. Micro-credentials and badges, common in the private sector and emerging in tertiary education, appeared in K-12 as signaling mechanisms for education versus the traditional diploma.

React and Return (Quick Recovery, Negative Attitude)

A relatively mild recession allowed schools to return to normal relatively quickly. There were adjustments made to accommodate the loss of learning in the following academic year. However, within two years the institutional grind of K-12 education returned to normal. Little attention was paid to improving responsiveness in the face of any kind of disruption.

Unlike the medical profession, where the pandemic caused a surge of career interest in the healthcare field, fewer and fewer people wanted to become teachers. The equity issues exposed during the pandemic were given lip service, and access to a quality education for many is still difficult. In spite of the lack of support from state and federal government, a few "shining star" districts, whose leaders were highly visible and effective during the pandemic, continue to lead their districts in closing gaps. However, for the most part, schools returned to business as usual, and it remains the core operating model.

Signals

The biggest signal for determining which scenario becomes plausible is the economy. A slow economic recovery would likely have a trickledown effect on education with respect to jobs and funding. A fast recovery could mean additional funding for schools to address problems of access and equity.

The shifting or hardening of political attitudes could also play a part. At federal and state level, ideological alignments and splits in the executive and legislative branches could play a key role in determining the level of resource allocation.

A more progressive approach to solving systemic problems could see funding increased and a new educational agenda being embraced. However, a state of partisan gridlock would ensure that little or nothing gets done. Finally, attitudes toward public education as part of a larger discussion on income inequality will determine plausibility of the scenarios, especially if it becomes a major talking point in the early years of the Biden administration.

- *In a rapidly changing world, how might the political agenda and philosophies of ruling parties impact the delivery of education in the classroom?*
- *How might local government authorities respond to educational concerns if there is indecision or gridlock at the national level?*
- *What other events must occur before society addresses systemic challenges in education, including teacher shortages and issues of access and equity?*

Jason Siko, Ph.D., is an instructional technology consultant for Wayne RESA, a regional service agency supporting districts in Southeastern Michigan, including Detroit. Jason was a secondary science teacher for 13 years and has held several academic and administrative appointments in teacher preparation programs and educational technology.

Principal's Morning Announcement—Public School 3.16, Brooklyn, New York, September 1st, 2025

By Alisha Bhagat

How might schools and relationships with the community of parents, educators, and students change in a post-pandemic future?

Public School (PS) 3.16, District 2, Brooklyn, NY

This vision of the future is inspired by my experiences as a parent and a futurist living in New York City. Starting March 16th, 2020, NYC public schools shut down and switched millions of students, parents, and teachers to remote learning.[28]

Principal's Morning Video Announcement, First Day of School, September 1st, 2025

"Good morning and welcome to the 2025 school year from myself and the staff of PS 3.16. We have sent your orientation packets via social media and traditional email. You can also view them on the school's YouTube, Google, Facebook, AppleView, Muskcast, and TikTok channels. Please take a moment to review some of the guidelines we are instituting this year to ensure that we can provide the most up-to-date educational content for you.

"Before we begin, let us observe our customary moment of silence for the many colleagues, classmates, and family members we have lost over the last five years.

"For those of you remaining in the city and in school, congratulations, you made it. Let us celebrate our accomplishments, and the milestones we have reached. Based on student feedback, we have changed the school mascot to the tardigrade, a micro-animal able to survive in extreme conditions. The student government will be crafting a new digital logo of our mascot.

"As you know, we have used every pandemic since 2020 to recalibrate our curriculum and focus on critical areas. As these viral diseases continue to adapt and change, so does our school! Here are the key items of note:

"Outdoor Time–We recommend you wear your personal protective equipment (PPE) at all times when going outside. I do want to point out that those of you who keep wearing the Plague Doctor outfits should knock it off!

"Over the past five years, the amount of public parkland available to you in New York City has risen over 50% as disused buildings and parking lots continue to be converted to green spaces. Many more streets are now closed to traffic, but we still recommend observing the public safety measures, even between pandemic events.

"Disaster Protocol—We are fully able to comply with the disaster protocol as set out by the state, be it extreme weather or pandemic related. When you are notified of a possible disease outbreak or disaster, please follow the protocol, collect your belongings, and head calmly to your designated meetup point.

"Meals—During this orientation week, in addition to your 'at home learning devices,' you will be issued a box of 'Ready to Eat' meals lasting one month.[29]

"Should another crisis emerge, you will be sent a sufficient amount of food so that you will not have to leave your home for weeks if needed. I'm also pleased to report that the cafeteria staff have developed delicious shelf-stable dehydrated meals in student-selected flavors including Nathan's hot dog, bagel with lox, pizza slice, and churro.

"Curriculum—We have almost completed our transition from a set curriculum of required courses to student-directed modules focused on addressing current societal needs. In addition to the core areas of study, we are offering even more new electives this year which Juniors and Seniors may select from. The range of these topics now includes urban farming, community engagement, the crypto economy, emergency health services, disaster recovery, climate science, caregiving, immersive media, and future studies.

"Social—As has been the case since 2020, we will not be holding the senior prom or any social dances. However, we will be allowing 'silent discos' where you may dance outside individually, with proper distancing, while listening to your personal musical choices via your own devices.

"While we cannot monitor out of scoool activities conducted in your personal time, we would strongly discourage students from organizing their own secret proms, survival parties, or 'another year alive' mass gatherings as have happened in previous years. We would remind you in the strongest terms that these continue to be illegal under NYC State law. We are all too well aware of the rise in infection rates and untimely deaths that can be directly attributed to such activities in previous years. Before thinking about organizing or attending such events this year, we would urge you to consider the risks to you, your friends, and your families.

"Finally, let me remind you of guidance from the New York Department of Health: YOU are your own safest sexual partner. Repeat—you are your own safest partner in this regard. Remember to wash hands before and after engaging in sexual contact—even with yourself.

"As you start your school year, remember, you students are the survivors and it is on you that we will depend to rebuild a world that's more inclusive, safer, and resilient than the past. Continue to adapt, flourish, and make us proud, class of 2026."

- *How might childhood and adolescence be different in the post-pandemic world?*
- *How might institutions such as schools have to change and adapt to life after the current pandemic?*
- *What things do we value and hope to keep the same about our children's school experience over the next decade?*

Alisha Bhagat is a futurist at Forum for the Future. She is passionate about working with organizations to help them think systematically about a more equitable and sustainable future.

After the Pause: The Unspoken Futures of Post-Pandemic Higher Education

By Alexandra Whittington

What are the most surprising or unexpected plausible future scenarios imaginable for the return to university beyond the pandemic?

Even before the pandemic, mainstream debate about the future of higher education tended to oversimplify the issue into a binary choice between online learning and face-to-face instruction. In practice, it is extremely optimistic to believe that things could be settled so easily. The pandemic, in unleashing the unthinkable, has set the ideal conditions for higher education to be completely transformed.

The unprecedented level of creativity needed to navigate the lockdown and reopening of universities has shown that there is more flexibility in our tertiary organizations than previously thought. This chapter presents scenarios for the possible future of higher education that emphasize high-risk, high-impact, low-probability potential outcomes as opposed to "business as usual" forecasts. Assuming that the pandemic has indeed created a "new normal," what might the university of the future look like?

The images of the future in these scenarios look nothing like the universities of today. They are meant to highlight the most extraordinary possible outcomes from the pandemic's vast disruption of higher education that started in 2020. Each one is written from a highly student-centric viewpoint, not truly accounting for how faculty or staff would respond. However, future scenarios offer the rare chance to encapsulate a serious visionary possibility for what could be. In the dark aftermath of the pandemic, it is only fair that we should get to dream. This chapter backcasts three extreme future scenarios (in reverse order) from their projected dates of 2030, 2025, and 2023.

Meltdown and Brain Drain (2030)

By the summer of 2021, the writing was already on the wall, but the reality had not yet sunk in. Western universities from the US to the UK and Canada found the enrollment of international students drop to almost zero. Historically, the budgetary and tuition structure of many of the most prestigious universities had long been bolstered by predictable waves of international tuition fees flowing freely from Asian nations such as China, the Middle East, and South America.

A potent mix of fear, economic fragility, and geopolitics suppressed international enrollment from 2020 through to 2025. In that period, American research centers suffered and in a short time the Science, Technology, Engineering, and Mathematics (STEM) workforce had actually shrunk. A post-Brexit UK saw a decline in students from the European Union (EU) as well as from the regular student source countries further east. Canada's more humane pandemic response and recovery helped the nation attract more students than other English-speaking countries.

Over the same period, China, and some of the least pandemic-ravaged Asian nations, enhanced their universities and began to attract more Western scholars to conduct research. A reverse brain drain was kicking into a higher gear for the next decade. Innovation, research, and academic clout shifted east because the money followed the students. As a result, by 2030, a shortage of qualified doctors was common in the West, which exacerbated the decline in the healthcare industry that followed the pandemic. The big STEM companies relocated to be near the universities where they recruited their future workforce—in countries like South Korea, India, and across the Asia Pacific region.

Climate Change Preppers (2025)

After the pandemic, experimental collectives began to appear in Europe and North America with the explicit purpose of preparing society for inevitable climate change impacts. They were similar to universities in the sense that they attracted young people, but these were people with refocused priorities; they wanted to figure out what to do with their lives while saving the planet. However, these collectives did not offer degrees or classes, as it was more of an opportunity to conduct practical environmental activism and research while exploring nature.

The pandemic was jarring too many individual members of Gen Z and those that came after them, and it seemed to have awoken something in their generational zeitgeist. After completing secondary education during the chaotic years of the pandemic period, many young people had lost their taste for formal schooling. A large number of them viewed the pandemic as a sign of how "on-the-brink" we really were as a species and, though it was too late to prevent the virus from becoming a pandemic, it felt like there was still enough time, and growing global momentum and support, to stop the climate crisis.

So, by taking over the abandoned facilities of universities who had moved exclusively to online education, self-organizing groups of militant climate change preppers made it their mission to research, advocate, and inform society about the coming apocalypse and how to prevent it. They wrote books, spoke out in public venues, hosted webinars, and unleashed social media campaigns. They put themselves to the test in extreme natural settings, camped out, and learned survival skills so that they could eventually teach others.

The preppers became experts in, and taught, first aid and first responder tactics—they practiced climate change rescue scenarios—simulating people trapped by wildfires and floods. Surviving the pandemic had made them more aware of how easily lives could be lost. Hence, as the global economy wavered between recession and depression for years on end, they were fearless and had nothing to lose or look forward to in terms of financial security or social mobility. The preppers were funded by royalties and fees generated by streaming the entirety of their activities live online as reality programming.

Lockdown University (2023)

The pandemic had the higher education system on a teeter-totter of online/face-to-face into 2023, then things leveled out somewhat. However, because business and the economy had been so severely impacted by the lockdown, new courses and areas of study were being requested by the students and their future employers. This new direction for higher learning was vital in preparing students to work in an unstable job market with frequent disruptions.

Business courses were retooled to offer expertise in touch-free customer service and delivery, for example. Students wanted support and coaching for online job interviews and how to network. Economics professors embraced increasingly important fields of research which sought to measure different forms of unpaid work, caring work, and housework as contributors to GDP.

Essential worker roles, which required no college degree, were gaining stature in the post-pandemic society. Some students were eschewing college altogether as the ideal job preparation path. Instead, growing numbers of young people enrolled at university to pursue personal learning goals. Many students planned on taking essential worker jobs after graduation, as those now paid more and could lead to further opportunities. In any case, ever since the US minimum wage was raised to over US$45 per hour in 2022, universities were eager to keep their students happy. Meanwhile, universal basic income had gone truly universal, and every nation now offered some kind of support since no one really had to go to college to get a job anymore. They did not actually have to work for money unless they wanted to.

So, universities were filled with people pursuing their own purpose but also wanting to give back in some meaningful way. The pandemic had renewed student interest in things like home economics and self-sufficiency activities such as gardening, cooking, and baking.

People wanted to know they could take care of themselves during any kind of shelter-in-place order. They also wanted to learn and teach others essential survival skills like foraging and carpentry. One popular focus was cosmetology, so that people could undertake their own beauty care regimes and cut and style their own hair. Demand rose for other pandemic-related subjects, like epidemiology and public health. This trend lasted for a decade in higher education, reshaping course offerings and scholarships for a generation.

- *Would English remain the universal business language if innovation, research, and development increasingly shifted eastwards?*
- *Could devotion to causes like climate change increasingly draw young people away from higher education and into practical activism?*
- *Is it possible for the pandemic to change economic foundations so much that college is no longer the key to a good future quality of life?*

Alexandra Whittington is a futurist, writer, and faculty member on the futures program at the University of Houston. She has a particular expertise in future visioning and scenario planning.

INNOVATION AND TECHNOLOGY

Beyond the Pandemic —All Change

By Roger Camrass

What changes might we see across political, economic, social, and technological domains in the next 12 months and 12 years?

The pandemic has accelerated change across the entire political, economic, social, and technological (PEST) spectrum. Major developments have been taking place in weeks or months rather than the years or decades that had previously been expected. Few events in history could prove more transformational at a global level.

No one can predict the exact outcome of the pandemic, especially over the coming months, but we need to consider the extraordinary rather than the ordinary in our business planning. Here are some predictions of what we might see, both globally and locally, in the near term, for example over the next 12 months, and over a longer time frame of 12 years:

In the next 12 months
- Digital leaders continue to stay ahead of traditional US Standard & Poor's (S&P) incumbents in market valuations. Following in the footsteps of Apple, Amazon approaches the two

trillion-dollar mark along with Microsoft. Old economy firms see a continuing decline in equity values.

- Global 1000 companies realize that it is impractical to even try and transform the core of their organizations to compete with the digital leaders. Instead, they focus on edge-based innovation projects.
- The way business is conducted changes for ever. Business travel declines by a third and a similar proportion of employees remain at home in the new age of distributed working.
- European debt rises to critical levels threatening the stability of the Union. The chief culprits are southern nations such as France, Spain, and Italy.

In the next 12 years
- More than 50% of city center offices are transformed into accommodation units. These co-living communities behave like villages with their own self-contained retail and leisure areas.
- The UK evolves rapidly to become a viable arts and crafts economy assisted by developments such as social clustering, 3D printing, and cloud platforms.
- Virtual reality will enable people to be in "two places at once" with dramatic consequences for the way we work and socialize.
- Hyper-personalization based on our own data enables a breakthrough in key sectors such as medicine where the efficacy of cures for chronic diseases improves by over 90%.

These predictions are based on fundamental changes taking place across the political, economic, social, and technological spectrum. Here is an overview of how such changes might take place.

Tectonic Movements in Global Politics

Whether China was negligent in its handling of the global pandemic will be an ongoing debate, especially in the US. For sure, in the near term, it seems likely to harden Western attitudes toward the Chinese government. Following the recent escalation of trade conflicts between the US and China, the pandemic could create a longer term and more tectonic shift in attitudes and political strategies between East and West.

At the European level, the pandemic has further exposed the economic and political differences between south and north, especially between Spain and Italy, and Germany and the Netherlands. The EU could face an existential crisis. It is unclear whether the northern nations will help bail out their southern counterparts. The debate will grow over whether they should even try given the fundamental gaps in productivity that are now increasingly evident. Brexit is declared by many in the UK as a positive move in terms of global trade and economic revitalization.

The Great Economic Clean Up

The pandemic is likely to accelerate the demise of some 50% of S&P incumbents who could vanish off the map in a matter of years rather than decades due to their inability to adapt. Newcomers might swiftly occupy their spaces. Despite the myriad of digital transformation programs across global corporations and government departments, numerous studies on innovation suggest that many have failed to deliver the promised returns, and little has changed. These monolithic incumbents have been designed for operational excellence. However, such approaches are no longer fit for purpose in many cases. In a world of increasing uncertainty, business models need to combine agility with efficiency.

The near death of many high streets and shopping malls since the start of the pandemic is just one illustration of just how broken many current business models are. Few existing players with a primarily physical presence have been able to respond at speed or innovatively to the sudden rise in online demand. The pandemic has exposed these weaknesses and is driving widespread closure or shrinkage of non-viable organizations in many sectors.

A New Social Order

The rapid advance and integration of several new technologies meant we were already progressing rapidly toward a world of hyper-personalization where every aspect of our lives is captured, stored, recalled, and analyzed. The pandemic has accelerated this process, with the prospect of universal tracking of individuals to trace contagion. There are mixed views associated with hyper-personalization, but the consensus is that data is the fuel of the digital economy and will become our most valuable personal asset.

The development and adoption of tools for analyzing personal data multiplied in the pandemic environment. Data protection frameworks such as the EU's General Data Protection Regulation (GDPR) could become rapidly outmoded in this new era. They may need to be revised fundamentally to accommodate this level of personal data capture by governments and the technology players who are penetrating every aspect of our lives.

The Technological Juggernaut

Over the last 20 years we have witnessed a first wave of digital technologies such as social media, smartphones, data analytics, and cloud computing. These have transformed many aspects of our lives and now enable billions of people to work comfortably from home as well as to interact with communities all over the world.

A second wave is in view that could bring about even greater change such as artificial intelligence (AI) and machine learning, 5G, augmented and virtual reality, the Internet of Things (IoT), 3D printing, and blockchain. We talk now about a verbal-visual-virtual revolution that could enable us to be in two places at once.

It is entirely conceivable that a factory near you could produce all the products necessary for a comfortable existence. Data analytics, AI, and machine intelligence could reduce drug development cycles from decades to years—or even months, especially where viruses and new variants are concerned. The combination of 5G, IoT, and AI are poised to accelerate the use of robotics and driverless cars, which could prove a life saver in the present environment.

Perhaps the most interesting change could be a possible transformation of today's rigid supply chains that would enable higher degrees of agility through a combination of IoT, 5G, Cloud, and AI. Considerable hope is being placed on 5G mobile communications technology with the potential to help transform sectors such as healthcare, logistics, construction, utilities, and agriculture.

New Ways of Operating in the "New Normal"

The sheer speed and scale of change and transformation taking place suggest that traditional business planning methods have no place in the fast-accelerating post-pandemic world. Instead, I believe that organizations need to adopt agile patterns of behavior based on a 20-year vision and a three-month operating plan.

- *How might corporate planning be affected by the pandemic?*
- *What types of business and government innovation are required to navigate through and beyond the crisis?*
- *How does the pandemic affect your personal view about life and the future?*

Roger Camrass is director of research at CIONET International and a visiting professor at the University of Surrey.

Crisis (危機) = Danger (危) + Opportunity (機): A New Renaissance

By José Cordeiro

Is the pandemic a source of global danger that also uncovers a great opportunity in the evolution of this planetary crisis?

The Chinese word for crisis has two characters (危機). The first character (危) represents danger. The second (機) can be interpreted as opportunity, change of time, moment, or chance. Even though the meaning of the characters can vary according to the context and nearby characters, the understanding of crisis (危機) as danger (危) plus opportunity (機) can help us analyze the present situation.

We are living through a historic crisis created by the pandemic and its aftermath, which implies present danger but also future opportunity. Even though the pandemic originated in China, it created a long-term global problem that requires equally far-sighted global solutions. The situation presents a fantastic opportunity to move forward together as one global family on our small planet, if we avoid the danger of standing divided against our common enemy. This probably represents the worst pandemic since the 1918–1920 Spanish flu, when up to 100 million people died, which was substantially more than the casualties in World War One, or even in World War Two.

Now, fortunately, exponential advances in science and technology might help to halt the spread of the virus, hopefully avoiding the grim milestone of millions more deaths, in a population much larger than existed in previous tragedies. In the great planetary war against this unseen enemy, many public and private responses have emerged and are continuing to evolve. Governments, large companies, small start-ups, universities, and even individuals continue to try and figure out how to control, cure, and eliminate it, along with current and future possible mutations. While the initial development costs have been high, they can be amortized quickly by mass-producing the best treatments across the planet.

Expectations are running high for the long-term effectiveness of the vaccines, although concerns remain over the speed of global roll-out. However, let's remember that when HIV and AIDS appeared, it took over two years to sequence the virus, with no treatments emerging for several years. Indeed, AIDS was considered the perfect disease, because it destroyed the immune system itself and basically constituted a death sentence for the patient, with no possible escape.

After years of research, the first treatments to control HIV were developed, with each treatment costing millions of dollars. Today, exponential scientific advances mean that HIV is now treated as a chronic disease with antivirals costing hundreds of dollars in richer countries, and only tens of dollars in poorer nations like India. Fortunately, it is also highly likely that in this decade, a vaccine will finally be discovered to protect people against HIV and definitively eliminate it.

Although it seems difficult to believe, thanks to the great exponential advances in science and technology, a range of vaccines have now gained regulatory approval and are in the process of global roll-out. Many countries have made incredible strides toward full vaccination of all willing members of the population. It is quite possible that this terrible pandemic will be remembered in the future for having been overcome with unprecedented speed.

The situation is providing a great lesson for humankind. It has shown that we must work together, because global problems require global solutions. Hopefully, the lessons learned, and collaborative approaches developed during this experience, will serve as a model for tackling other global challenges such as climate change, food poverty, and terrorism.

There will almost certainly be new pandemics in the future. However, the expectation is that we will be more prepared to overcome them quickly thanks to exponential technologies and accleraterd global research and development collaborations. Given the exponential pace of development of the underlying technologies, it is entirely feasible that we could sequence the next pandemic virus in just two days, and the following one in two hours. Contrast that with a two-week time frame in the current situation, two months for SARS two decades ago, and more than two years for AIDS. Not only are the timescales for fighting diseases being reduced exponentially, but the costs also are falling dramatically.

A New Renaissance

History is littered with examples of incredible advances that resulted from crises. The Black Death, or Plague, was the most fatal pandemic recorded in human history, with up to 200 million deaths across Eurasia, peaking in Europe between 1347 and 1351. The Renaissance started in Italy partly as a response to this incredible disaster. Subsequently, the Great Plague of London from 1665 to 1666 killed an estimated quarter of the population of London. This was followed by the Great Fire that lasted five days and destroyed the medieval City of London inside the old Roman city walls. This incredible human tragedy was the opportunity to rebuild London, its Cathedral, the Royal Observatory, and Royal Society, among many other landmarks.

During his Cambridge isolation in the Great Plague, Sir Isaac Newton developed his theories on calculus, optics, and the law of gravitation. Similarly, William Shakespeare wrote *King Lear* during previous bubonic plagues in London and was also inspired to create other masterpieces like *Romeo and Juliet* and *Macbeth*. The hope is that the 2020s might equally be a decade full of incredible opportunities for all humanity.

Should advances in science and technology progress at the expected rate, and human ingenuity be unleashed and supported, then this will be the decade when the first humans land on Mars; when artificial intelligence passes the Alan Turing Test and reaches human intelligence levels; and when longevity escapes velocity and radical life extension might finally be achieved to bring about the death of death. Perhaps most importantly, for the first time in history, according to the World Bank, by 2030 we could eliminate poverty in the world and deliver the Sustainable Development Goals.

The ability to develop technologies differentiates humans from other animals, and exponential technologies are our great ally to accelerate positive changes. Technology helps humans be more human, and thanks to technology we keep moving up the pyramid of Abraham Maslow's hierarchy of needs. In the next ten years, I believe we are could see more technological changes than in the last 100. Let's not waste this crisis, and together let's move forwards and upwards to a better world for all.

- *How can we avoid wasting this crisis and use it as a global opportunity for a New Renaissance?*
- *Could new exponential technologies prevent future pandemics?*
- *In what ways might technology advance more in the next decade than it did in the entire previous century?*

José Cordeiro is a director of the Millennium Project. He is also a fellow of the World Academy of Art and Science, vice chair of HumanityPlus, founding faculty at Singularity University at NASA Research Park, Silicon Valley, and a guest lecturer at many institutions. He studied engineering at MIT and business at INSEAD.

How the Pandemic Has Become an Accelerant for Virtual Presence

By Cathy Hackl

How might the pandemic speed up our virtual presence and the creation of a "metaverse" of shared virtual spaces where humans and machines can interact?

World shaping events have a history of changing the way humans operate. After the attack on Pearl Harbor, the US transformed its whole codebreaking operation. More recently the 2020-21 pandemic, which kept us socially isolated, has made us rethink how we can do our jobs, visit family, and entertain children without physical contact.

Immersive technologies like augmented and virtual reality (AR/VR) show us we don't have to be together physically to feel like we are working with, or connected to, others. In VR, we can obtain information and create memories of experiences in the same way as if acting them out in real life. Virtual presence already reaches far beyond what we see on our screens. For example, there are pillows for people in long distance relationships that light up when a person lays their head on one. Smart watches and fitness bracelets buzz on our wrists to notify us of incoming messages, issue reminders, or send coded "haptic taps"—gentle physical nudges to give us directions so we don't have to look at our phones.

Lockdowns may have provided time to immerse ourselves in virtual worlds, but how might this form of togetherness persist? The technology is evolving so that a virtual presence can form around us, utilizing all our senses: touch, smell, taste, hearing, and, of course, sight.

Imagine cooking dinner while talking to your mom on video. The swivel camera automatically detects who's talking. There is a sensor above the stove sending the chemical signature of the aroma so your mom can smell your cooking through a scent generation device at her end. You feel a squeeze on your arm through the haptic sensors in your shirt sleeve. It's your mom, lovingly saying "good job on dinner," without speaking a word.

Robotic Telepresence

When Business Breakthrough University in Tokyo canceled live graduation due to pandemic concerns, they used telepresence robots to perform the ceremonies. The robots consist of a remotely operated mobile platform, and a computer tablet at human head height level, allowing the student operators to see and be seen at the graduation event. In future, it won't be uncommon for grandma to have a home robot. Family members could access it remotely to check in, watch a movie with her, or help around the house.

Similar to how we fly drones with smartphones, robots will increasingly have simple interfaces. Slip on smart glasses to "see" through the robot's eyes. Sensors on the glasses will pick up hand and body movements to move the robot naturally, as if there in person.

Extending Our Realities

The pandemic is ushering in an era of increasingly "real" and highly experiential virtual events. For example, the 2020 Educators in VR International Summit was held not as a replacement for a canceled real-world event, but as an intentionally immersive VR conference. The summit was hosted on multiple virtual social and educational platforms. Participants noted how much it was like attending a real-life conference, aside from the lack of a swag bag. Participants had the ability to choose to focus on what is happening on stage, or to wander off to chat with people they just met.

As a result of the pandemic, virtual conference organizing has become an in-demand job, like social media managers after the advent of Twitter and Facebook. As more events move online, VR companies could explore offering more integrations between their platforms. Swag bags might be shipped to those who pay for upgraded tickets.

With the emergence of more platforms like Facebook Horizon that let users create their own virtual environments and games, we may see a further merging of our digital and physical identities. Some analysts, such as social VR thought leader Navah Berg, see this next era of social VR as a possible scenario of how the future of social media and community might evolve.

Sports teams increasingly understand that some fans want to live the game through their devices. This desire was exacerbated by the inability to attend live events during the pandemic. Soon fans will be able to experience the game through haptic feedback to feel what it's like to strike a ball like a pro. Mixed reality visuals using tools like AR will allow us to watch the ball fly virtually across the living room.

Virtual telepresence could provide a sense of the fans for players. In future, fans can be virtually broadcasted to arena seats, their cheers echoing out through stadium speakers. Instead of appearing on the big screen, super fans can be part of the dug-out experience through holographic telepresence technology. Why pay for box seats when you can virtually sit with your favorite players?

Into Virtual Worlds

During the pandemic, many doctors and therapists moved to tele-medicine apps to continue seeing their patients. Patients are becoming increasingly comfortable with the service and like the convenience of telemedicine so much that many want to continue using it after the pandemic. Imagine sitting on your couch but seeing your therapist's office around you. You feel calm as you smell the lavender candle she always has burning. Your therapist sits across from you virtually.

Remove your smart glasses and you're back in your living room as if you had just walked in the front door.

American rapper and singer-songwriter Travis Scott's 2020 "Astronomical" concert in Fortnite had more than 12 million people play along to his larger-than-virtual-life performance. The show highlighted how music, gaming, and virtual presence continue to merge. Epic doesn't see this as a one-off; they see it as the future. Imagine being able to hear and feel the concert as though you were up on stage with the band, crowd-surf with the lead singer, and feel the adrenaline rush of 100,000 people singing along to your biggest hits, all while sat on your sofa on the other side of the planet.

World catastrophes like pandemics show us our weak spots but they also give us the opportunity to come together and innovate. Many technology companies are racing to redefine themselves for a post-pandemic future. My hope is that humanity will leverage these technologies to help make our worlds more productive, more connected, and less isolated. Virtual telepresence lets us push boundaries and allows us to be present in the convergence of both the physical and virtual worlds.

- *Which sectors could be re-energized in the post-pandemic period through the use of immersive technologies?*
- *What propositions might retailers of home-help immersive applications and devices develop for different generations?*
- *What role might virtual worlds play in different parts of society, business, leisure experiences, communities, and families?*

Cathy Hackl is a technology futurist and business strategist. She specializes in the impact emerging technologies like AR, VR, and artificial intelligence are having on communications and business.

How Digital Ecosystems Might Shape the Post-Pandemic Recovery

By Greg Wasowski

How might digital ecosystems evolve to help accelerate post-pandemic recovery, and what do leaders need to understand to assess the possible industry impacts?

This chapter shares a possible scenario of how digital ecosystems might evolve over the next three to five years. It aims to help leaders in particular to explore the potential impacts for their organizations. I use Gartner's definition of digital ecosystems as "an interdependent group of actors (enterprises, people, things) sharing standardized digital platforms to achieve a mutually beneficial purpose."

The pandemic has changed our world. Dealing with the aftermath could be the imperative of our times. More than ever, we need to make our businesses more resilient and relevant to customers. Organizations will need to rebalance priorities and figure out how to operate in new ways. Many will accelerate their path to digital transformation, seeing it as key to survival and long-term prosperity.

As understanding of digitalization matures in small and large companies alike, and as digital literacy rises, our capacity to prioritize and focus digital transformation investments should increase. This combination of understanding and literacy will hopefully provide the foundations for effective and productive participation of organizations in digital ecosystems. These, in turn, should provide many with a platform for better collaboration, rapid innovation, and greater productivity.

As a basis for my exploration, I suggest four focus areas for leaders to consider while evaluating the impact of digital ecosystems on their businesses as they plan for recovery and growth.

New Ecosystems

There is now a range of technology companies with well-established digital ecosystems. The technology industry has pioneered the development of digital marketplaces and ecosystems. In the post-pandemic era, the next wave of innovation might come from the non-tech organizations as they seek to refocus themselves around an efficient digital and data-centric operating model.

The pandemic triggered an accelerated refocusing of priorities and is driving changes in needs, buying behaviors, and service expectations of businesses and end consumers alike. A shift in organizational thinking is also being driven by a combination of ongoing pandemic risks, potential for supply chain disruption, working from home, and social distancing requirements for workplace redesign. There is a clear and growing need for new ways of organizing to ensure entities stay relevant to customers, and are prepared to change ever more rapidly in response to uncertainty and volatile market behaviors.

In the emerging business environment, we are likely to see an increase in public and private collaboration, which is already helping accelerate key initiatives such as vaccine and treatment development and distribution. Retailers and manufacturers have started seeing the value of being part of a faster and more multidimensional network, accelerating creation and distribution of goods such as critical medical supplies. There is also a growing understanding that ecosystems can foster inter-organizational collaboration and potentially generate new roles that could provide work to employees displaced by the pandemic and technology innovation.

For financial services firms, the need to adapt to a more competitive post-pandemic environment, and the resulting imperative for more fundamental business transformation, are already accelerating changes in their approach to digital initiatives. This is translating into a greater willingness to expand their investments in areas such as robotic process automation, artificial intelligence (AI), cloud computing, and API-driven transformation.

Innovation is coming from FinTechs, whose growth is often accelerated by their ability to start with customers' jobs-to-be-done and their application of technology to create new business models, as well as the incumbent players that invest in creation and acceleration of partnerships, ecosystems, and new models such as Banking as a Service. For many in the sector, collaboration is seen as the fastest, and potentially only, route to meet rapidly evolving customer expectations across commercial and private banking, lending, wealth management, and insurance.

Similarly, biopharmaceutical companies are increasingly looking at digital ecosystems as vehicles to deliver faster innovation and achieve performance superior to businesses that operate more independently. Organizations across all industries are already starting to uncover the potential of digital in improving the customer experience, deepening intimacy, streamlining decision-making, and enhancing learning.

Empathy

As organizations look to stabilize and redesign operations in the post-crisis environment, empathy will be key to building new relationships internally and externally. Many employees, partners, suppliers, and customers may have suffered high levels of stress and fatigue during the most intense periods of the pandemic. This next era of business will require strong personal skills and emotional sensitivity to enhance collaboration, work across multiple partner companies, and forge strong relationships with existing and newly created business units.

Design thinking was already becoming more widely used and its adoption is likely to increase in the pursuit of faster product, service, and process redesign. This approach encourages organizations to ask the fundamental "why?" question repeatedly and make sure they truly understand their customers, share those insights with other ecosystem participants, and prioritize their needs. After the stabilize and re-open phases of pandemic response, a clear understanding of what employees and customers need should help companies navigate the economic recovery, prepare to operate faster, and become more digitally adept.

"Empathize" is the first stage of the highly effective digital thinking model proposed by the Hasso-Plattner Institute of Design at Stanford (d.school), followed by phases of Define, Ideate, Prototype, and Test. In a post-pandemic world, cost pressures are expected to increase and we could see greater risks resulting from launch delays or poorly targeted products and services. If we fail to see the world through our users' eyes, understand what they see, feel their emotions, and experience life as they do, the sets of products and offerings we develop could become obsolete quickly. Hence, we can expect to see more organizations leveraging design thinking to create sustainable solutions that exhibit desirability, feasibility, and viability.

Agility

Leaders of many organizations around the globe have had to change the way their businesses operate almost overnight. The pandemic has resulted in jobs being disrupted, new skills being developed, and new business and operating models introduced. All of these changes are likely to continue for some time and are only possible with an agile mindset. Agility is defined as the ability to react to sudden changes in demand or the operating environment. This is a crucial capability that needs to be incorporated in all digital transformation agendas, including the fundamental mechanics of ecosystems.

For agile acceleration to be successful, organizations may need to go back to the drawing board and rethink and refocus their overall strategy. This will need to be accompanied by a reworking of business and operating models, and core processes, supporting the organizational design and the enabling culture. This also means rigorous prioritization of key initiatives and an enabling commitment to the notions of trust and transparency as staff are asked to let go of much of what worked and underpinned their effectiveness in the past.

As we deal with the aftermaths of the pandemic, agility also means learning how to make decisions faster with a more decentralized workforce, how to work more effectively, how to engage in new ways with customers and partners, and how to fulfill our broader responsibilities to society. For the latter, many are being guided by the United Nations Sustainable Development Goals as an overarching framework to decide where they can make the biggest contribution. The focus on agility in building or redesigning digital ecosystems can enable all participants to respond quickly to new insights or challenges. Done well, it should deliver higher quality end results on shorter timelines, while reducing risk and costs of extensive revisions and reworks.

Trust and Transparency

As we build digital ecosystems and create new opportunities, we must be aware of the complex risks to be managed and the need to build ecosystems on solid fundaments of trust. More than ever, a high level of transparency between customers and business partners is required across the ecosystem's lifecycle, including vision, product strategy, service design, and the customer experience.

Trust and transparency are not just "feel good" sentiments. Making full use of the platforms behind the ecosystems (both in the technical and broader sense of the word) require business and technical leaders to focus on communicating transparently, and engaging intelligently with technology. Trust is becoming the most important currency influencing customer engagement, brand values, and operational agility. The emergence of Chief Trust Officers, who orchestrate trust beyond the technical domain, could play a crucial role in more effective planning, valuation, security and privacy design, platform verification, revenue models, crisis management, and resiliency.

Resilience

The pandemic has highlighted the importance of resilience, developed through effective foresight and contingency planning. Hence, the next chapter in the use of digital ecosystems will require us to learn from past mistakes and increase our focus on resilience. The promise of the emerging wave of integrated digital services offered by new and existing players is that they will help the ecosystem drive value, link previously disconnected industries, and generate new revenues. All these benefits will be accessible only if we start building resilience from the onset, and by doing so, increase our competitive edge.

To achieve these ambitions, resilience will need to start being implemented as a key pillar of business strategy, as important as financial management or product innovation, rather than a set of rudimentary survival measures. The imperative is for leaders to grow their resilient foundations, allowing key resources to be allocated to the right initiatives, and aligning them to the goals of accelerated transformation rather than post-development risk mitigation. The impacts of the pandemic on business operations have emphasized the need for new resilience policies to place a stronger focus on workforce management, platform security, business continuity, and cash flow.

Ultimately, those who build empathy, agility, trust, transparency, and resilience into digital ecosystem strategies will be better placed to to survive, thrive, and lead the next wave of customer transformation.

- *How might customer expectations shift in the coming years?*
- *Could digital ecosystems help you survive, thrive, and transform?*
- *What is the biggest threat for your company right now and which of your previous business imperatives need to be rethought?*

Greg Wasowski is a strategist and a solution designer. In his current role at Salesforce, he focuses on developing business and technology strategies that help partners reach product–market fit faster. He is a design thinking practitioner and loves exploring the unknown, challenging conventions, and driving innovation.

From Surviving to Thriving the Pandemic: Digital Transformation in Action for Connected Communities

By A. Reza Jafari

How can the public sector in urban and rural communities respond to the challenges of serving diverse populations with civic and social services while also dealing with the impacts of the pandemic?

Cities of all sizes and shapes around the world absorbed and responded to the unprecedented shock of the pandemic with different degrees of preparedness. The shock clearly manifested itself over the fundamental elements of every civic structure and in the socio-economic foundations of urban and rural communities alike.

Major high-density cities in every continent responded with different emergency plans and varying degrees of resource deployment, leading to a wide range of outcomes. These communities came into the crisis with different levels of experience in dealing with major natural and human crises. However, this pandemic had unexpected characteristics that caught many civic leaders and millions of their citizens off guard and unprepared.

Some believe that digital transformation can play a greater role in future responses and the enhancement of community preparedness, and the foundations are being laid. During the past few years, several cities of varying sizes around the world have embarked upon the goal of digital transformation into connected or smart communities.

Connected communites are defined as an ecosystem platform of multi-stakeholders. This platform utilizes integrated information and communication technology systems and data analytics to transform culture, structure, operations, economic development, and citizen engagement. The goal is to manage complexity and dynamically improve and enhance the quality of life.

The 2020 pandemic wrought havoc across society and in the functioning of cities. The supply chain of civic and social services was disrupted, creating uncertainty and anxiety. As we look to the future, humanity cannot afford another such experience of widespread unpreparedness and extreme vulnerability.

In response to the challenges, here I present six critical elements of an action planning framework to help our communities be better prepared and ultimately thrive in the new normal. This framework is designed to enable affordable, equitable access through the digital transformation of our cities and communties with the deployment of a range of information and communication technologies, applications, services, and devices. Let's examine each of the six elements and the potential benefits.

Public Safety and First Responders

An investment priority for national and local governments should be to build the required systems infrastructure, information flows, and human capabilities. The goal is to enhance the resilience and agility of national emergency and defense forces in dealing with future pandemics and other nation-scale emergencies. Such a strategy would in turn help shape a coordinated framework of international and intergovernmental relationships and information sharing—something that seems sadly lacking in the global response to the pandemic.

In combination with other public safety infrastructure, targeted technology applications in particular would increase the capacity for timely and life-saving responses to natural and human emergencies and disasters—as well as supporting efficient resource deployment. For example, with timely information provision, on-location treatments and medical interventions could be made possible.

Governmental Agencies and Departments

The reality for much of the public sector worldwide is that the cost of dealing with the pandemic is driving budget shortfalls and cuts, thus reducing the availability of financial and other resources. Meaningful technology deployment would allow for the automation and self-service provision of social and civic services that do not require face-to-face contact between agency staff and the service recipients. Digital citizen engagement with elected officials could dramatically increase the potential to reflect societal views and perspectives to our leaders. Ultimately, the productivity and efficiency of government agencies could be enhanced significantly.

Healthcare Organizations

With a new connected service paradigm, healthcare organizations could reimagine the delivery of quality care and outcomes for patients and providers and better manage pandemics, other unexpected events, and ongoing healthcare crises. Telehealth and telemedicine enabled by artificial intelligence and augmented reality could enable remote monitoring of patients and advisory care for preventive medicine.

Such a model requires new policy and regulatory frameworks for governing the relationships between patients, providers, and payers. New collaborative public–private partnership models could also be enabled. Private foundations such as the Bill and Melinda Gates Foundation are already offering matching funds for connected health initiatives. So in the US, for example, implementaton could be accelerated by combining this targeted philanthropy with federal agency support for the establishment of telehealth systems. Such grants and funding are currently available from the US Department of Health and

Human Services, the Federal Communications Commission, and the United States Department of Agriculture (USDA).

Educational Institutions

The challenge highlighted by the pandemic is to ensure universal digital inclusion, raise digital literacy, and ensure a similar standard of education across all strata of society. A connected communities platform would offer affordable, reliable, and secure broadband services and devices to every teacher and student regardless of socio-economic stratification.

Again the key is effective partnership with the matching funds for digital inclusion and distance learning systems, with example initiatives from the likes of the Organization for Economic Co-operation and Development (OECD), and the Bloomberg, Rockefeller, and Gates Foundations. This needs to be coupled with grants for the establishment of distance learning systems from the US Department of Education and USDA. At the delivery level, it requires targeted balancing of investment by educational institutions, state legislatures, and local governments between "bricks and mortar" and hybrid virtual learning and workforce platforms.

Effective delivery would involve helping teachers and faculty members to acquire new skill sets and expertise for designing and delivering their educational content for equal and effective pedagogical outcomes. Teacher and skill shortages could in part be overcome by trained and qualified remote learning specialists.

Community Service Organizations

In many nations, communities in rural areas in particular often rely upon the service of non-profits and philanthropists to provide resources and services in support of local residents. In this scenario, with public funding under even more pressure, organizations such as senior citizen centers, assisted living homes, low-income shelters, and community service centers could find a connected community platform invaluable. It could prove particularly valuable in increasing the effectiveness and efficiency of core activities such as fundraising, promotion of and access to services, and volunteer recruitment.

The Private Sector

Digital platforms are already transforming the world of work and the workplace. Existing companies and the new generation of employers are increasingly adopting remote working and delivering products and services online or via third party fulfillment. This will reduce their capital expenses for real estate and other central office and infrastructure costs. A digital operating model will also reduce the time and cost of commuting, accelerate the time to market for new offerings, and potentially enhance productivity, profitability, and sustainability.

Clearly, the suggested framework is not exhuastive and would need to be adapted to the needs of each community where it was adopted. Equally, it would need to take account of diverse local factors such the environment, socio-economic indicators, political structure, and economic outlook. Criticallly, the adoption and implementation of any such model should involve citizen engagement of the community at every level.

- *What are the potential community-based solutions in our preparation to fight the next global pandemic and human crisis?*
- *How can we create collaborative ecosystems to enhance innovation and increase its contribution to humanity?*
- *What role can we as individuals play in the innovation ecosystem as a contributor to and participant of the global community?*

Reza Jafari is the chairman, CEO, and founder of e-Development International. He is also the co-managing editor of "Connected City Blueprint", a Trustee Board member of Chesapeake College, co-chairman of the Connected City Advisory Board, and a Board member of the India, China, and America Institute.

A Viridian Aurora

By Frederic Balmont

What if the solution to our biggest global challenges was to combine ecology with technology in a liberal way?

Today, in 2026, some green and blue lights are rising over the land: blue for technology, green for ecology. As always with the dawn, we can also witness some scarlet shades. What has happened in the past five years that has brought about such a global shift?

Death as Equalizer

Some historians, like Victor Davis Hanson, have emphasized a link between death and democracy. So, for example, the Athenians would have been considered politically equal because of their equal exposure to death as citizen soldiers. Another aspect is the unifying power of a common enemy; an enemy who can enslave or kill you. This idea has greatly inspired popular culture, as embodied in movies and drama series such as *Watchmen* and many others.

The Power of the Smallest

Prior to the pandemic, we already had a terrible common enemy: death. In response, a sophisticated ideology, transhumanism, tried for years to federate our world around the struggle against death, with growing but limited success. Death is too abstract, and its daily faces are so varied. It is the Many Faced God for sure! Death is hidden by its omnipresence.

However, the smallest "living" creature, a primitive "killer," comprising a few DNA fragments in a simple structure, produced the most significant health effects seen in a long time. A disruption, in all sectors of social life, has occurred without possible backtracking.

Remember 2020, When Illusions Collapsed

Political leaders, and some happy few, who thought they were taking advantage of this world, tried to manage economic problems by preserving pre-pandemic governance models. The smartest knew that this battle was already lost: we had to move forward.

Why? Because people saw that a lot of work was not essential, that ecological collapse could be avoided by slowing down, that the economy had not collapsed, that the rich and the poor alike could be killed by a virus, but that it was still better to be rich. In addition, we have seen that social activity, jobs, and life skills were not what made you rich. We can stop most of the planes, motorcycles, and cars; work less and more remotely; reconnect with others even if we are far away; and emphasize a "quality of heart" rather than the pursuit of consumption. Many working poor have been the new heroes of this crisis, alongside scientists, physiologists, and nurses.

2022, When the Ordinary Heroes Make a New World

Our everyday heroes were exposed to many aspects of death, they lost their dear friends and family members, and they too died. Others had been isolated, confined. They lost their jobs. They learned injustice. This proximity to death led these heroes to endure deprivation, risks, and the acute mental, physical, emotional, and economic post-pandemic aftermath. They learned to read terror on the faces of previously dominant people, whose merit and alleged legitimacy of commanding and owning the world were brutally questioned.

These valued skills and this new symbolic legitimacy were decisive enough for societies to refuse to go back to the old order. They said no! No to continuing to be forced to destroy ecosystems through our way of life. No to working in vain and for nothing. No to being continuously kept away from political decisions.

2023 Massive Riots, Rebellions, Financial Panics, and Emergence of Alternative Models

The more conservative and oppressive the governments, the more violent and determined the riots: the financial markets demonstrated their irrationality in times of crisis and their inability to meet human needs; governments showed that they are mainly structured to conserve power—meaningless power.

The worst impacts were felt when the US, after rescuing the economy through massively increased public debt, demanded colossal efforts from the weakest, with a call to global morals and solidarity. This took the form of severe austerity plans and the sale of public goods. Of course, those who had financed growth in US debt through the financial markets were the same private interests which had benefited from tax exemptions. They also benefited from delivering the public rescue plan, and from contracts for provision of public services and infrastructures.

The sporadic riots of 2019, such as yellow coats, umbrellas, etc., were early warning signs of what was to come. The virus has chemically precipitated a change in social imagination. Alternatives now appeared logical: universal wages, Tobin taxes, research funding, and an emphasis on a more ecologically aware civilization. Some countries started on this path during the pandemic. Even the Pope was quick to plead for global action in this direction. Globally, it is now more widely understood that ecology is the best way to avoid pandemics, biotechnologies are the best way to cure them, and human development is a very effective way to increase the value of everyone's life.

2024-2026 the Second Enlightenment

After the turmoil of 2020–23, there was widespread agreement that we needed more science, intelligence, and peace if we are to save and protect lives. Across society, we needed deeper knowledge of ecosystems, of viruses and their mutation mechanisms, of the human brain, and of the means for society to survive. In this quest, technology was seen a helpful and necessary tool. As a result, we increased our power, and this allowed us to live slowly, with more humanity.

We are in an era when open sources, the pooling of knowledge and resources, and accelerated research in the Nano-Bio-Info-Cogno (NBIC) arena provide appropriate solutions to many global challenges. Educated citizens help governments in making good decisions. While it is true that we have lost a lot of jobs through the use of artificial intelligence (AI) and automation, we have also been freeing up creativity and the availability of talent for other useful social activities. We have realized that the world had previously wasted so much talent and potential. As a result, we see the birth of a new global confidence in human genius, taking us a few steps toward a new fraternity.

Today, in 2026, there are still obviously authoritarian temptations here and there, with proposals for withdrawal to the past, and a return to premodern forms of social and spiritual life. But these ideas are born out of fear, with a goal of maintaining strict hierarchies which dominated and would still dominate. These old solutions are not easily rejected, and the new world is taking time to develop. However, in this new enlightenment, we understand that, ultimately, we have a simple choice between a walk toward the viridian dawn, or a long journey into the dark ages. We make this choice of inclusive progress because it is in the dark that we remember that we are made for light.

- *Does our need to understand living things and ecosystems happen through the development of new technologies, or through a return to an alleged intuitive wisdom of the earth?*
- *Does navigating this crisis require strong and authoritarian leaders or the harnessing of collective intelligence?*
- *What if the most useful work for humanity was to finance the reduction of our parasitic activities?*

Frederic Balmont is a work inspector at the Ministry of Labour. He is a member of the French Transhumanist Association, a graduate in philosophy and psychology, and an author.

FUTURE FRAMEWORKS

Framework 1: Grand Challenges—Emerging Global Opportunities and Critical Risks

By Rohit Talwar

Where might we find the most exciting opportunities in a post-pandemic future and what risks should be on our radar?

Introduction

We are beginning to appreciate that the pandemic will continue to evolve for some time to come and that we must adapt to the idea of living with the virus on a long-term basis. Acknowledging this changing context across all walks of life, our attention is gradually shifting to focus increasingly on the broader landscape and the medium- to long-term future. Governments, organizations, civil society, and individuals are beginning to ask what the wider set of opportunities and risks are that could shape the operating environment over the next 12 months to 10 years?

Typically, the resulting insights are helping organizations to identify the critical driving forces that will be used to build scenarios, map emerging opportunities, guide risk management plans, and shape new strategies. Individuals are also finding that a deeper awareness of these future factors can help them and their families navigate this emerging landscape of opportunity and risk.

To help identify some of the critical driving forces, set out below is a concise summary of a range of important factors shaping the future across five key domains. These are economy and finance; government and governance; individuals and society; science and technology; and sustainability, energy, and environment.

In each case, a range of the key underlying factors and forces are set out, and core opportunities and risks are contrasted for each of them. The factors and the analysis of opportunities and risks are drawn from our own work and a variety of other sources including the Millennium Project's 15 Global Challenges and discussions on a possible United Nations (UN) Office of Strategic Risks,[30] the UN Sustainable Development Goals,[31] and the Stockholm Resilience Centre's work on Nine Planetary Boundaries.[32]

Economy and Finance

Factor	Opportunities	Critical Risks
Economy	Sustainable and inclusive global growth	Systemic meltdown of financial markets and economies leading to prolonged depression
	Reduction of debt dependency for individuals and nations, particularly among the most economically unstable and indebted nations	Regular disruption and recessions in debt laden, economically fragile, and politically unstable nations
	Global alignment of taxation systems and rates to remove anomalies and minimize potential for tax avoidance and evasion	High levels of personal and national bankruptcy
	Testing and establishment of new strategies to achieve a workable balance between individual and corporate taxation and the requirements to deliver public services, manage national finances, and maintain and enhance infrastructure	Growing country dependency on international bailouts that impose hardships and require forfeiture of key national assets and resources in return
		Countries compete to offer the lowest individual and corporate tax rates, with new tax havens emerging globally
	New models emerging for running pension systems that maximize participant protection while also controlling the overall costs and risk of system collapse	Increasing difficulty in funding and delivering public services, infrastructure, and crisis responses
		State pension systems collapse in the face of rising life expectancy and extended periods of retirement
	Greater focus on, and incentivization of, sustainable growth investment by businesses and financial institutions	Erosion of public employment
Incomes and Wealth	Global uplift in living standards and rebalancing of wealth distribution across society	Increasing consolidation of wealth among the top 1–5% globally
	Continual increase in minimum income levels and abolition of subsistence level wages	Lower incomes, increasing disparity, declining living standards, and rising inequality for a growing number in society
	No one left behind	Rise in the numbers of those who now live "outside the system" with no income
	As jobs become obsolete or automated, widespread experimentation with, and adoption of, guaranteed basic income schemes to help workers transition between careers	Zero or minimal support for most of the unemployed
		Rising crime levels
	Deeper society-wide education in managing personal finances and planning for the future	Growth in the shadow economy

Factor	Opportunities	Critical Risks
Financial Systems	Effective monitoring and control across all financial markets and asset classes globally	Collapses of financial markets due to debt, derivatives, and other complex financial instruments
	Tighter regulation and greater transparency of derivatives and other high risk and complex financial instruments	Financial market failures leading to global contagion, depression, regular more regional and national recessions, stalled development, widespread corporate failures, high long-term unemployment, and reversal of social progress
	Best practice country-level financial market controls evolve to a consistent level globally	
	Emergence and adoption of more efficient, and lower cost approaches to funding new ventures and growth of existing businesses	Major financial market failures drive nations into bankruptcy, cause runs on banks and financial institutions that eventually fail, and catalyze societal collapse
	Digital transformation of financial markets to improve transparency and access—e.g. enabling fractional share ownership and individual participation in more lucrative financial opportunities normally reserved for the wealthy and institutions	Individuals largely priced out of most forms of investment, receive low or negative interest rates, and inflation drives down the real values of most people's savings
	Enforcement of transparency and explainability requirements as greater use is made of artificial intelligence (AI) across financial markets	Crypto markets remain largely unregulated, leading to high rates of fraud and manipulation, asset theft, rising volatility, market meltdowns, large losses for unprotected investors, and outright crypto bans in some nations
	Effective crypto asset regulation and customer protection frameworks, and rising levels of crypto literacy, help accelerate adoption and enable the wider population to participate in the opportunities presented by Decentralized Finance (DeFi) in particular	Major investors and institutions drive out smaller retail investors from crypto asset markets and gradually erode the underlying principles of establishing transparent, immutable, censorship-free, independent, community governed digital currencies
	Adoption of cryptocurrencies as legal tender helps poorer nations see multiple benefits—appreciation in the value of national reserves; stabilization of economies; reduced dependency on other nation's currencies; paying down debt; increasing the inflow and value of foreign remittances; and raising living standards	Dramatic decline in the value of cryptocurrencies that are used as legal tender leads to national economic collapse and reversion to Yuan or US Dollar adoption with high transition costs and domestic upheaval
	Central Bank Digital Currencies (CBDCs) help stabilize economies and reduce transaction costs	Rising concerns and evidence of government misuse of citizens' financial data arising from the adoption of CBDCs

Factor	Opportunities	Critical Risks
Technological Disruption	Nations establish long-term transition plans to address the shifts that will result from increasing automation and widespread adoption of AI to replace human roles—encompassing sectoral development, long-term workforce planning, skills and retraining, transitionary incomes, digital literacy, and employment Population-wide education programs to help citizens learn about disruptive new and emerging technologies, understand the changes they are bringing about, and see the opportunities and challenges for society and those whose jobs will be most affected Wide-ranging provision of training opportunities for displaced workers	High levels of social unrest, with aggression and customer boycotts directed at technology companies and organizations pursuing large-scale automation and job elimination Increased demand for social security benefits Highly automated, digitally enabled decentralized autonomous organizations (DAOs), and firms with highly reduced headcounts move to low tax nations Economic hardships lead to population-wide worsening of mental and physical health with declining life expectancy Rising trust deficit, suspicion, and crime across society

Government and Governance

Factor	Opportunities	Critical Risks
Political Governance	Drive for greater governmental transparency and citizen choice over how they are governed	Expansion of autocracy and totalitarian regimes
	Increasing multinational connectivity and coordinated action on global grand challenges	Decision-making increasingly opaque and consolidated in the hands of the political and financial elites
	Effective scrutiny of physical and digital elections by independent observers	Rising nationalism with growing fragmentation and a lack of coordination on responses to global issues
	Technology increasingly used to help draw electoral boundaries on a transparent and equitable basis	Gerrymandering of electoral districts becomes commonplace, reducing public trust in electoral processes
	Mass drives to register those who are eligible to vote	Growing concern over vote rigging, and ballot fraud increases social division and renders some countries, cities, and towns ungovernable
	Workable incentives to encourage mass voter participation	Increasing barriers to voter registration
	Digital technology used to help build population-level collective intelligence, increase participatory decision-making, and create deeper cross-societal understanding and appreciation of multiple perspectives on key issues	Widescale voter suppression driving public unrest and delegitimization of election results
		Systematic erosion of freedom of speech
Global Institutions	Strengthening, modernizing, and increased inclusivity and representation of current global institutions	Loss of institutional mandates, countries withdrawing, and destabilizing collapses of some current groupings
	Development of new mechanisms to cope with the requirements / challenges of a rapidly changing and increasingly interconnected changing world	Existing institutions struggle to handle modern-day global issues that don't sit well in their current scope, e.g. cybercrime, crypto assets
	Key groupings such as ASEAN, OAU, EU, GCC, SCO, G77, G20, and G7 establish progressive, citizen focused agendas	Internal tensions and complexities of aligning member states gradually erode the operation and effectiveness of these groupings and hinder international collaboration
	Growing emphasis on global intelligence sharing, collaboration, and coordination on addressing critical global challenges and opportunities	International institutions de-legitimized in the eyes of nations and corporations, leading to increasing violation of standards and norms
	Development, adoption, and enforcement of strong common ethical standards in fields such as science, medicine, and new technologies such as AI	Decline and collapse of adoption of and adherence to ethical standards in science and technology research and development

Factor	Opportunities	Critical Risks
Conflict and Stability	Expansion of peace and mediated solutions	Escalation of existing conflicts and proliferation of new ones
	New approaches used to resolve intra-national conflicts at every level	Return to Taliban rule in Afghanistan creates a safe harbor and breeding ground for radicalized groups and destabilizes the entire region
	Workable solutions found to long-standing disputes over borders, water access, mineral rights, religious differences, and historic issues	Rising tensions and military engagement between major powers and among smaller nations
	China's Belt and Road Initiative drives economic development and enhances stability in participant nations	Corporations increasingly drawn into conflicts as participants and/or funders
	Tight controls over the use, role, and oversight of private military contractors and corporations in conflicts	Increasing privatization and outsourcing of physical and cyber conflict—to military contractors, corporations, and even other nations
	Internationally agreed controls over the use of technologies such as AI, drones, and robots in warfare	Belt and Road Initiative increases tensions between China and the US in particular. Participant nations face sanctions from countries opposed to expansion of China's global trade infrastructure, economic power, and political influence
	Gradual reduction in the need for and stockpiling of nuclear weapons	
	Effective global controls and inspection regimes prevent the emergence of new nuclear powers and restrict the actions of existing ones	Unresolved and increasingly aggressive conflicts lead to use of nuclear weapons
	The use of aid seen as increasingly more effective than direct intervention, with a focus on equal treatment of women and minorities, capacity building, access to education, job creation, human rights, and peaceful approaches to internal conflict resolution	Weapons stockpiling continues and increasing number of state and non-state actors are believed to have nuclear capabilities
		Nations become ever more cautious in the allocation of aid budgets for fear of the support being misused or channeled to radicalized organizations

Factor	Opportunities	Critical Risks
Terrorism	Experimentation with, and adoption of, non-violent mechanisms to engage terrorist organizations in resolving conflicts, reaching binding agreements, and allowing independent monitoring of commitments

Coordinated intelligence led reduction of international terrorist organizations and activity

Greater information sharing and cross-organizational working at the national level leads to more effective preventive action against terror groups and lone wolf actors

Workable mechanisms found to reintegrate terrorists back into society once sentencing is completed

Rethinking of prisons to prevent them becoming recruiting grounds for new terrorists

Expansion of education and economic opportunity offering an alternative path for potential terrorist recruits | Rising level of terrorist activity undertaken by international networks, domestic groups, and lone wolf actors

Terrorist groups increasingly reluctant to join resolution discussions and largely ignore agreements

Growth of political, cultural, and religious terrorist groups and non-state terrorist actors

Rise of new domestic extremist and terror organizations, sometimes with close links to political parties and key politicians

Lack of coordination and information internationally and locally enable terror groups to recruit and grow unchecked

Prisons increasingly become prime locations for recruitment and radicalization of would-be terrorists

Bleak economic outlook and feelings of disenfranchisement, oppression, and exclusion drive growth in terrorist recruits |
| Global and National Foresight | Globally conducted horizon scanning and scenario planning exercises used to identify and coordinate responses to emerging opportunities and high-impact risks

Countries establish robust national foresight programs which draw from and contribute to global horizon scanning initiatives

Politicians introduced to the nature and value of foresight approaches in policymaking

Policymakers and civil servants trained in the use of foresight approaches to inform policymaking, strategy development, and operational delivery | Nationalistic approaches lead to narrower world views, poor collaboration, inevitable surprises, and piecemeal responses to global issues

Patchy adoption and use of foresight programs, with strong central control of scope, agendas, and outcomes restricting the value of the work undertaken

Missed signals lead to foregone opportunities and more severe impacts of new risks

Short-term focused policymaking allows critical societal challenges to evolve unchecked and creates a negative legacy for future generations |

Individuals and Society

Factor	Opportunities	Critical Risks
Population	Stable and sustainable population growth Advancements focused on enabling education, income support, and services for the disadvantaged across the planet	Unsustainable and irregular patterns of population growth Dangerous levels of resource depletion through poor management of population-wide food programs
Health	Establishment globally of robust health systems with universal access and quality of life improvement for all Effective use of technology and data to enhance patient outcomes, increase the focus on wellness and prevention, and accelerate medical and pharmaceutical research Targeting of resources toward conditions and diseases most prevalent in poorest nations Emphasis on mental health and wellbeing	Unequal provisions, worsening health outcomes, and declining life expectancy in underserved communities Research largely focused on the needs of the wealthiest Under-investment in key technologies leads to inefficient use of resources, less effective monitoring of population and individual health, and suboptimal care Mental health issues underfunded and increasingly stigmatized
Education	Consistent, lifelong, and life-wide provision Modernization of learning programs to maximize individual potential and fulfillment using a blend of physical and virtual learning experiences	Growth in undereducated, disenfranchised, and disengaged segments of society Education systems focused on creating economic units of production using rote learning, and highly automated and depersonalized learning approaches
Women	Accelerated global drive toward equal rights, opportunity, and rewards Equal access to education and training at all age levels Massive reduction of crimes against women through greater societal education and behavioral nudges, supported by severe penalties	Growing disparity of gender status, opportunity access, and rewards Legislation moves backwards in some states to reduce the rights and freedoms of women Crimes against women increase, deprioritized by law enforcement with poor conviction rates and a decline in reporting

Factor	Opportunities	Critical Risks
Diversity	Inclusion and respect for all enshrined across policymaking and societal norms Merit-based access to employment and promotion opportunities Positive action to overcome imbalances in salaries, benefits, and representation at different levels within organizations Truly neutral criminal justice models emerge which focus solely on the individual and the alleged offense	Widespread marginalization, systemic and institutional bias, and unequal treatment for different segments of the population Systemic barriers and biases hold back key groups and lead to: i) large-scale employee rejection of the worst offenders; and ii) negative employer brands Minorities of all kinds increasingly over-represented at each level of the criminal justice system, leading to rising disenfranchisement
Ethics	Enhancement, creation, and encouragement of local, national, and global ethical frameworks	Ethical erosion, self-serving outlooks, and societal collapse
Trans-national Crime	Sharing of criminal intelligence between agencies globally Coordinated and effective detection and suppression Renewed faith in criminal justice systems Belief that politicians, public officials, and the police are acting in society's best interests	Unchecked growth in the scale, scope, and sophistication of activities Penetration of mainstream sectors and financial flows Growing criminal success in public sector procurement Rising criminal influence over politicians, judicial systems, public officials, and the police

Science and Technology

Factor	Opportunities	Critical Risks
Scientific Progress	Global coordination and collaboration focused on society-wide benefits across all key fields of scientific endeavor Greater sharing of knowledge and IP, with an increased amount of scientific research made public on an open-source basis Effective global control frameworks put in place around the risks, safety, ethics, and societal value of scientific research	Increasing control of IP by nations and businesses Profit maximization becomes the primary driver of publicly and privately funded research programs Widening gap between nations on capabilities and scientific knowledge access Uncontrolled development leads to high-risk research projects with potentially damaging social implications and impacts
Scientific Outcomes	Exponential pace of development and combination of key scientific fields to create abundance and tackle societal grand challenges Greater cross-societal voice in highlighting and prioritizing public funding of science and technology research Strong oversight of corporate R&D agendas	Growth in malicious developments and applications such as bio-weapon attacks, denial of digital services, harmful AI bots, hacking, and security breaches Major accidents such as particle accelerator failures, leading to incidents such as creation of anti-matter or a black hole
Pandemics	More globally coordinated early warning and response mechanisms Better prepared nations and international institutions Effective procedures in place to mobilize key resources, facilities, and fast track procurement Robust testing of procedures to ensure the ability to take early action to control viral spread; prove test, trace, and vaccination management systems; stress test robustness of supply chains; address the economic impacts; and communicate clearly and consistently with citizens	More uncontrollable and frequent outbreaks Inadequate and inefficient pandemic response mechanisms Increasing pressure on health systems Declining political motivation, economic capacity, and societal willingness to take each new pandemic seriously Rising cross-societal costs—social cohesion, public distrust, national and personal finances, business viability, physical and mental health, and capacity to invest for the future

Factor	Opportunities	Critical Risks
Artificial Intelligence (AI)	AI well understood across society AI harnessed in service of—and to the benefit—of humanity Strong global governance and ethics frameworks guide development Full explainability of AI decision-making becomes a regulatory requirement for all applications Robust plans / mechanisms in place to address impacts of AI on employment—encouragement of new job creating sectors; worker retraining; support for new venture creation and self-employment; guaranteed basic incomes during career transition; counseling for displaced workers; and public education	Massive adverse impact on jobs and living standards AI technology and the commercial rewards dominated by a few giant corporations, investors, and nations Uncontrollable development and a spread of unethical applications Widespread use of AI by criminal organizations Unbounded military adoption of AI leads to more conflicts and lethal outcomes Government and society unprepared for unintended consequences of future advanced forms of AI and rogue AI applications
Nanotechnology	Pathway to abundance, smart materials, and "nanofacturing" Smart physical solutions to critical global challenge Lower environmental footprint of nano-engineered solutions	Malicious applications of the technology (the "gray goo" problem) Rise of nano pollutants Unintended consequences lead to major societal disruption and human harm
ICT Infrastructures	Global convergence and interoperability of technology platforms Advanced software development tools enhance reliability and verifiability of applications Distributed platforms and applications provide transparency and resilience Enhanced forms of system, network, and data security enabled through AI and quantum tools and solutions Effective management of security across all elements of networks	Vulnerabilities created by ungoverned and unregulated autonomous systems and poorly structured distributed systems Emphasis on delivery speed leads to more critical failures Hacker's use of new technologies leads to regular extinction level security breachesGrowing theft of personal and organizational data and assets Devices connected at the edge of networks and Internet of Things become key security vulnerabilities
Planetary Management and Protection	Greater understanding of the universe applied to enhance life on Earth and increase planetary protection Global agreement and coordinated action on long-term planetary protection goals Increased allocation of funding for planetary protection research, countermeasures, and remediation	Poor coordination, many nations refuse to act on risks Extinction level asteroid collisions, weakening of the Earth's magnetic shield, poll reversal, and solar gamma-ray bursts Areas of the planet rendered uninhabitable, high population casualties and economic losses, and large numbers of displaced people

Sustainability, Energy, and Environment

Factor	Opportunities	Critical Risks
Sustainability	Achieving the UN Sustainable Development Goals prioritized by every nation and business Sustainable protection of people, planet, and economic stability placed at the center of decision-making for national and local government and business Deep education of society on sustainable lifestyles, with regulation and incentives to guide businesses and households toward true sustainability Global best practice sharing	Widespread decline in, and irreversible damage to, ecological environments, living standards, public health, food security, viability of nations, and economic stability Decline of biodiversity Dangerous and unmanageable legacy left for future generations Unsustainable practices lead to major safety issues and failures in key industries, with severe penalties and remediation costs
Energy	Global transition to low cost, sustainable, and renewable generation and distribution Energy access and availability as a right, with growth in local / domestic generation Range of technologies used to generate energy from waste, heat, and motion in buildings, homes, and public areas	Crumbling, underfunded, expensive, fragile, ecologically unsound and destructive energy solutions with uneven access Little incentive to fund pursuit of renewable and localized energy solutions in economic adversity Collapse of many fragile and outdated energy infrastructures
Climate Change	Global commitment to, and coordinated action on, stretching targets Emissions reduction targets incentivized and embedded in regulation Acceleration in achieving true carbon neutrality by 2025–2030 by nations, cities, communities, and corporations Investment in research, experimentation, and deployment of workable solutions for both prevention and mitigation	Catastrophic global warming, increasing frequency of climate related disasters from flooding to forest fires, and irreversible damage to ecosystems Key ecological resources emit more CO2 than they absorb Adverse climate effects lead to severe health challenges, premature deaths, millions of environmental refugees, and large negative economic impacts
Clean Water	Universal access acknowledged as a right Low-cost innovative solutions replicated globally to accelerate achievement of SDG targets Novel solutions to develop ultra-low cost and easily distributed solutions	Reluctance to invest, and inefficiency of actions taken, leads to worsening of health and increased mortality rates Loss of wildlife and severe adverse impact on crop health and food quality, availability, and price

Factor	Opportunities	Critical Risks
Atmospheric Management	Enhanced monitoring and reduced impacts through scientific advances and geo-engineering solutions Demonstrable improvements in public health	Increasing air pollution and declining biospheric integrity Stratospheric ozone depletion / atmospheric aerosol loading Oceanic acidification
Biodiversity	Diversification of food crops Active promotion and protection of biodiversity	Species reduction / overreliance on fewer food cropsand loss of critical ecosystem services provided by biodiversity
Land Use	Focus on one planet living and accelerated shift to sustainable agriculture and smart farming Green belt expansion Rainforest preservation	Adverse land use changes Unconstrained and poorly regulated over-construction Disruption of biogeochemical flows

The factors presented above are by no means exhaustive. However, they hopefully provide a starting point for scanning of emerging opportunities and risks. Of course, the way in which we approach addressing the opportunities could create unintended risks. Equally, addressing the risks could open up a whole new set of opportunities.

- *Which future factors will have the most significant bearing on your personal life plan and your organization's strategies?*
- *Which opportunity areas create the most attractive prospects?*
- *Which risks present the biggest challenges to your personal ambitions and the organization's strategic assumptions?*

Rohit Talwar is a global futurist and the CEO of Fast Future, where he focuses on helping clients explore the emerging future, respond to global opportunities, and identify and manage risks on the horizon.

Framework 2: The Technology Timeline—Advances Shaping the Next Decade

By Rohit Talwar and Karolina Dolatowska

What are the technologies we should have on our radar as we map out strategies for the next 5–10 years and beyond?

We are constantly bombarded by talk about building back better and the new normal. At the heart of most of these conversations is the notion that new and emerging fields of information technology in particular will enable a better future through the transformation of every aspect of our lives, society, business, and government. In response, some see a promising future filled with possibility, hope, and progress. Others worry about deep surveillance and increasing control of our lives, a loss of privacy, the rise of social scoring of citizen behavior, and the large-scale replacement of humans by exponential advancing and ever smarter technologies.

For us, the key to determining what our individual and collective responses might be is to make sure we are: i) investing the time to understand this array of technologies; ii) exploring the ways in which they might be used in the wider environment, in our sector, and by our organization; and iii) assessing the resulting impacts that could emerge across society.

As a starting point for further research and evaluation by the reader, we have set out below a table of developments that are already emerging or that we think will be entering into the marketplace over the next ten years and beyond. These are drawn from our own work and a range of other sources that are listed at the end of this document.

We have broken the technologies down into three broad time frames offering best estimates of when these technologies might reach 30% market penetration. These cover the next two years, two to five years, and five to ten years and beyond. Of course, we cannot be precise about these time frames, as technological advances and breakthroughs can happen much faster or slower than originally anticipated.

The pandemic has seen the acceleration of developments that were previously considered several years away. Of course, some might already be working with advances that we have put in the five-year time frame. Others might take far longer to act on technologies that we anticipate going mainstream in the next two. We believe that an understanding of the technologies is far more important than in trying to achieve precision on when they might hit the market.

We have also grouped these technologies under the eleven categories, namely: artificial intelligence, machine learning, and robotics; user interface and experience; software development and applications; infrastructure, ecosystems, and IT operations; communications, networking, and cloud; Internet of Things (IoT); computer architecture; security; blockchain and crypto assets; digital marketing and digital advertising; and digital commerce. Naturally, many different segmentations are possible here and there are overlaps between categories, however, we hope the ones chosen prove helpful as a starting point.

Category	0–2 Years	2–5 Years	5–10 Years +
Artificial Intelligence, Machine Learning, & Robotics	AI Ethics & Governance Frameworks	Affective Computing (Recognition & Processing of Emotions & Feelings)	Artificial General Intelligence
	Cognitive Algorithms	AI Application Marketplaces	Artificial Superintelligence
	Cognitive Assistance	AI Application Specific Integrated Circuits (ASICs)	Augmented Cognition
	Cognitive Automation		Emotional AI
	Cognitive Insight	AI Platforms as a Service	Explainable AI
	Computer Vision	Ambient Computing	Miniature AI
	Deep Neural Networks	Augmented Intelligence	Neuromorphic Computing
	Distributed / Blockchain-Based AI Platforms	Cloud-Based AI Services	Neuromorphic Hardware
	Facial Recognition	Composite AI (Integration of Multiple Approaches for One Application)	Quantum Machine Learning
	High Dexterity Physical Robotics		Responsible AI
	Machine Learning & Deep Learning	Constraint Satisfaction Problem (CSP) AI	Self-Replicating & Generating AI
	Medical Robotics	Decision Intelligence	Smart Dust (Microscopic AI Sensor Chips)
	Natural Language Processing – Interpretation & Generation	Edge AI	Technological Singularity
	Real-Time Prediction	Explainable AI	
	Reinforcement Learning Algorithms	Generative AI / Confrontational Networks	
	Robotic Process Automation	Human Level Robotic Dexterity	
	Rule-Based Systems	Ingestible Robots	
	Symbolic AI	Knowledge Graphs	
		Smart Robots	
		Swarm Robotics	

Category	0-2 Years	2-5 Years	5-10 Years +
User Interface & Experience	Augmented & Virtual Reality (AR/VR)	3D Sensing Cameras	Artificial Sensing Skin
	Biometric Authentication & Interfaces	Advanced Biometrics	Augmented Cognition
		Bionic Eyes	
	Brain-Computer Interfaces	Digital Identities	Bidirectional Brain-Machine Interfaces (BMI)
		Exoskeletons	
	Chatbots	Extrasensory Computing	Holographic Pets as Voice Interfaces
	Conversational User Interface		
		Implantable Mobile Phones	Implanted Brain Control Interfaces
	Epidermal (Human Touch) VR	Multisensory AR/VR	Privacy by Design
	Eye Tracking Technology	Olfactory Analytics	
	Mixed Reality Environments	Smart / Computational Clothing	
		Smart Tattoos	
	OCR/ICR/HWR	Voice-of-the-Customer Solutions	
	Speech analytics for Customer Services		
		Wearable Brain Control Interfaces	
	Virtual Beings / In-App Customer Personas		
	Virtual Customer Assistants		
	Visual Search		

Category	0-2 Years	2-5 Years	5-10 Years +
Software Development & Applications	3D Object Modeling Advanced CRM Advanced Visualization Algorithm Exchanges API Management Automated Code Refactoring Automation of Application Development Environments Autonomic Computing Citizen Development 2.0 Data Simulation Engines Dynamic Taxonomy Platforms Enterprise Open-Source Repositories Graph Analytics Low- / No-Code App Platforms Microservices Next-Gen Enterprise Resource Planning (ERP)	Advanced Quantum Software Development Kits Edge Computing Full Enterprise Integration Hybrid Quantum / Classical Algorithms Hypothesis-Driven Development Quantum Simulators Semantic Computing Small Data Fully Automated AI Code Testing	Automated Enterprise Operations Modeling & Simulation Automated Integrated Application & Business Model Development Automated Quantum Application Development Confidential Computing Enterprise Automation as a Service Self-Maintaining / Configuring / Updating / Replicating Application Ecosystems Synthetic Data Voice & Gesture Driven Application Development Zero Error Code Verification

FAST FUTURE

Category	0-2 Years	2-5 Years	5-10 Years +
Infrastructure, Ecosystems, & IT Operations	Application Performance Monitoring Suites	AI-Based Infrastructure Installation and Operations Verification and Monitoring Application Release Orchestration	AI for IT Operations (AIOps) Platforms
	Container Management Tools	Continuous Compliance Automation	AI Managed Dynamic IT Service Catalogs
	DevOps Toolchains	Data Sanitization	Autonomous Testing
	Digital Sustainability Monitoring & Management	Desktop as a Service	Chaos Engineering
	Disaster Recovery as a Service	DevOps Value Stream Delivery & Management Platforms	Continuous Quality
	Enterprise Digital Rights Management	DriveScale Composable Platforms	Front End as a Service
	Everything / Anything as a Service (XaaS)	Enterprise Information Management Programs	Immutable Infrastructure
	Infrastructure as a Service	High Performance Computing as a Service	IT Environment & Energy Systems
	Intelligent Data Centers	Fully Automated Data Centers	Model-Based System Engineering
	Multisourcing Service Integration	Green Infrastructure	Performance Engineering
	Serverless Computing	Hyper-Converged Infrastructure	Platform Ops
	Software-Defined Infrastructure	Infrastructure Automation	Programable Infrastructure
	Storage as a Service	Managed Hosting	
		Service Meshes	
		Modular / Containerized Data Centers	
		Site Reliability Engineering	

Category	0–2 Years	2–5 Years	5–10 Years +
Commu-nications, Networking, & Cloud	5G Networks	6G Networks	7G & 8G Networks
	Cloud Application Discovery	AI Network Traffic Analysis	Cloud Center of Excellences
	Cloud Management Platforms	Balloon Powered Internet	Converged Cloud Management
	Cloud Robotics	Cloud Data Protec-tion Getaways	Data Lakes
	Cloud Security	Globally Unified Communications	Fully AI Defined Networking
	Cloud Service Brokerage	Green / Low Power Communications Architectures	Intercarrier Service Automation
	Cloud Testing Tools & Services	Network Segmenta-tion & Slicing	
	Grid Networking	Next Gener-ation Video Conferencing Quan-tum Communication	
	LA / WAN / MAN / NAN		
	Low-Earth Satellites	Tactile Internet	
	Megascale High Throughput IP Networks	Standards for Current & Futures Technologies	
	Mesh Networks	Telepresence Communication Robotics	
	Microwave Communications		
	Network Function Virtualization		
	Network Manage-ment Automation		
	Optical Networks		
	Private, Public, & Hybrid Clouds		
	Software-Defined Networking		

Category	0–2 Years	2–5 Years	5–10 Years +
Internet of Things (IoT)	3D Printing Connected Vehicles IoT-Based Remote Control Apps IoT Fleet Management IoT Integration Managed IoT Connectivity Services Roll-out of Sensors & Intelligent Devices Sensored Infrastructure & Roadways Smart Cities	4D Printing Digital Twin of The Person Edge Analytics Event Stream Processing IoT Application Development Platforms IoT Authentication IoT Edge Architecture IoT Environment Monitoring & Management IoT Security IoT-Enabled Applications	Asset Performance Management Digital Threading IoT for Customer Services IoT-Enabled Products as a Service Smart Governance of Digital Twins Thing Master Data Management Things as a Customer

Category	0-2 Years	2-5 Years	5-10 Years +
Computer Architecture	Exascale Computers High Performance Computing High-Bandwidth Memory Multicore Next-Gen Enterprise Technology On-Chip Memory Universal Memory Venture Architecture Hardware as a Service	AI Optimized Storage Systems Emerging Non-Volatile Memory (NVM) as a Memory Device Glass-Based Data Storage Green Computing Architectures Grid Computing Massive Multicore Processors Microelectromechanical Systems Molecular / Bio-Chips NVM as a Storage Device Onboard AI Diagnostics on Computer Chips Optical Computing Quantum Sensing Spintronics	AI Optimized & Self-Configuring Hardware Application / Domain Optimized Hardware Brain Like Computing DNA Computing / Data Storage Data Adaptive Hardware Neural Network Computing Quantum Annealing Quantum Computing Self-Healing Architectures Topological Quantum Computing Water-Based Data Storage

Category	0–2 Years	2–5 Years	5–10 Years +
Security	Cloud Access Security Brokers Cloud Security Assessment DDoS Defenses Document-Centric Identity Proofing Endpoint Protection Platforms Firewall as a Service Hardware-Based Security In-App Protection IoT Security Network Access Control Network Firewalls Network Security Policy Management Secure Enterprise Data Communication Security as a Service Security Cross-Cutting Web Application Firewalls	Browser Isolation BYOD / BYOPC Security Cloud Native Data Loss Prevention Cloud Security Posture Management Container & Kubernetes Security Content Disarm & Reconstruction Device Endpoint Security for Frontline Workers Multi-Cloud Key Management as a Service Secure Instant Communication Secure Web Getaways Security Rating Services Serverless Function Security Threat Intelligence Platforms Zero Trust Network Access	Automated Business Email Compromise Protection Cloud Data Backup Enterprise Key Management Format Preserving Encryption Fully AI Managed Integrated Security Environments – Data, Applications, Infrastructure, Devices, & Communications Robotic Data Loss Prevention Secure Access Service Edge Unified Endpoint Detection, Responses, Management & Security

Category	0–2 Years	2–5 Years	5–10 Years +
Blockchain & Crypto Assets	Blockchain Application Platforms	Advanced Blockchain-Based UX/UI	AI Generated Blockchain Applications
	Crypto Asset Consensus Mechanisms	Blockchain-Based Data Security	Automated Blockchain App Testing & Due Diligence
	Cryptocurrencies	Blockchain Customer Services Applications	Automated Interoperability of Applications Across Blockchains
	Decentralized Applications (DAPPs)	Blockchain Enabled IoT	
	Decentralized Finance (DeFi) Applications, Platforms, & Tools	Blockchain Exchanges	Automated Oracle Updating
		Blockchain Interoperability	Blockchain Enabled Decentralized Supply Chains
	Digital Assets – Utility Tokens & Stable / Meme / Privacy Coins	Blockchain Managed Services	Decentralized Autonomous Organizations
	Digital Tokenization of Physical Asset / Commodity / Security Tokens	Blockchain Oracles	
		Blockchain Platforms as a Service (PaaS)	Full Blockchain-Web Interoperability
	Hot / Cold Wallets	Central Bank Digital Currencies (CBDCs)	Fully Decentralized Web
	Ledger DBMS	Decentralized / Self-Sovereignty Identity	Postquantum Blockchain
	Non-Fungible Tokens (NFTs)	Decentralized Artificial Intelligence (AI)	Privacy Enhancing Computation
	Permissioned Blockchain	Decentralized Content Distribution	Source Multiparty Computing
	Proof-Of-Stake Consensus	DIY No Code / Low Code End User DAPP Development	
	Proof-Of-Work Consensus	Fully Traceable CBDC Transactions	
	Smart Contracts	Layer 2 Solutions (Parachains, Sidechains)	
	Zero-Knowledge Proofs	Smart Contract Oracles	

Category	0-2 Years	2-5 Years	5-10 Years +
Digital Marketing & Digital Advertising	Ad Blocking Auditory Analytics Brand Safety Management Conversational Marketing Customer Journey Analytics Dynamic Digital Content Management Influencer & Advocacy Marketing Location Intelligence Mobile Marketing Analytics Multichannel Marketing Over The Top TV Advertising Perspective Analytics Proactive Communications Applications & Services Real-Time Marketing Sentiment Analysis Social Analytics Social Media & Marketing Automation	Account-Based Marketing Platforms Ad Verification & Viewability Advanced Supply Side Bidding Content Micro Personalization Customer Data Self-Management Platforms Identity Resolution Identity-Based Segmentation (Micro segmentation) Insight Engines Machine to Machine Advertising Master Data Management of Customer Data Mobile Wallet Marketing Multichannel Marketing Hubs Multitouch Attribution Smart Consent & Preference Management	Attention Purchasing Algorithms Blockchain-Based Advertising Customer Communications Gateways Allowing Only Permissioned Marketing Customer Data Ethics Data Clean Rooms Deep Personification Fully AI Automated Marketing Hyper-Personalized Communications Overlay of Customer Images on Characters in TV Programs Personalization Engines

Category	0–2 Years	2–5 Years	5–10 Years +
Digital Commerce	API-Based Digital Commerce Customer Journey Analytics Customer Messaging Applications B2C Dynamic Pricing Customer Psychographics Customer Service Analytics Digital Preference Management Digital Shelf Analytics Live Commerce Price Optimization & Management for B2B Recurring Revenue Management Shoppable Media Smart Check-Out	AI Consent & Performance Management AR / VR Immersive Commerce Augmented Reality for Customer Support Contact Center as a Service Customer Data Platforms Customer Engagement Hubs Digital Ethics Distributed Order Management Enterprise Commerce & Service Management Platforms Progressive Web Apps Smart Customer Identity Access Management	Composable Commerce Customer Service Multi-experiences Payment as a Packaged Service Personalization Engines Services Co-Creation Thing to Thing Commerce

- *Which technologies are currently expected to have the greatest impact on your organization?*
- *How frequently does the organization scan for emerging technologies and what scanning processes are in place?*
- *How does the organization determine the scope and time frame for its technology scanning?*

Rohit Talwar is a global futurist and the CEO of Fast Future with a particular focus on the impact of emerging technologies on individuals, society, businesses, and governments.

Karolina Dolatowska is a foresight researcher and the business manager at Fast Future.

Sources for 'Framework 2: The Technology Timeline– Advances Shaping the Next Decade'

Bill Halal – Forecasting Global Transformation – *https://www.billhalal.com/blog/forecasting-global-transformation/*

Builder – 21 Technology Milestones We Will Achieve By 2030 – *https://www.builderonline.com/products/home-technology/21-technology-milestones-we-will-achieve-by-2030_c*

Cult – Tech's "Next Big Thing": 20 Technologies & Innovations to Know About From 2022 to 2030 – *https://cult.honeypot.io/reads/20-technologies-&-innovations-2022-2030/*

Deloitte – Horizon next – A future look at the trends – *https://www2.deloitte.com/uk/en/insights/focus/tech-trends/2020/horizon-next-a-future-look-at-the-trends.html*

Future Timeline – Future Timeline – *https://www.futuretimeline.net/blog/computers-internet-blog.htm*

Futurism – Things to Come: A Timeline of Future Technology – *https://futurism.com/images/things-to-come-a-timeline-of-future-technology-infographic*

Gartner – Hype Cycle for Agile and DevOps, 2020 – *https://www.stackstate.com/news/gartner-mentions-stackstate-in-2020-devops-hype-cycle*

Gartner – Hype Cycle for Artificial Intelligence, 2020 – *https://www.gartner.com.au/en/articles/2-megatrends-dominate-the-gartner-hype-cycle-for-artificial-intelligence-2020*

Gartner – Hype Cycle for Blockchain Technologies, July 2020 – *https://www.gartner.com/en/documents/3987450/hype-cycle-for-blockchain-technologies-2020*

Gartner – Hype Cycle for Cloud Security, 2020 – *https://www.gartner.com/smarterwithgartner/top-actions-from-gartner-hype-cycle-for-cloud-security-2020/*

Gartner – Hyper Cycle for Communication Service Provider Operations, 2019 – *https://billing.gotransverse.com/images/gartner-hype-cycle.png*

Gartner – Hype Cycle for Customer Service and Support Technologies, 2020 – *https://www.gartner.com/en/newsroom/press-releases/2020-09-07-gartner-says-customer-service-&-support-technology-*

Gartner – Hype Cycle for Digital Commerce, 2020 – *https://www.gartner.com/en/documents/3988357/hype-cycle-for-digital-commerce-2020*

Gartner – Hype Cycle for Emerging Technologies, 2019 – *https://blogs.gartner.com/ smarterwithgartner/files/2019/08/CTMKT_741609_CTMKT_for_Emerging_Tech_ Hype_Cycle_LargerText-1.png*

Gartner – Hype Cycle for Emerging Technologies, 2020 –*https://www.gartner.com/ smarterwithgartner/5-trends-drive-the-gartner-hype-cycle-for-emerging-technolo- gies-2020/*

Gartner – Hype Cycle for Endpoint Security, 2020 – *https://www.addvalue.com.br/ endpoint-security-2020/*

Gartner – Hype Cycle for Human Capital Management Technology, 2020 – *https:// janzz.technology/janzz-named-as-a-sample-vendor-for-skills-ontologies-in-gartner-hype- cycle-for-hcm-tech-2020/*

Gartner – Hype Cycle for IT in GCC, 2019 – *https://www.gartner.com/en/newsroom/ press-releases/2019-10-14-gartner-s-2019-hype-cycle-for-it-in-gcc-indicates-pub*

Gartner – Hype Cycle for Network Security, 2020 – *https://www.hillstonenet.com/blog/ gartner-hype-cycle-for-network-security-what-you-need-to-know/*

Gartner – Hype Cycle for Supply Chain Planning Technologies, 2020 – *https://omp. com/gartner-hype-cycle*

Gartner – Hype Cycle for Supply Chain Strategy, 2020 – *https://www.gartner.com/en/ newsroom/press-releases/2020-09-09-gartner-2020-hype-cycle-for-supply-chain-strategy- shows-internet-of-things-is-two-to-five-years-away-from-transformational-impact*

Gartner – Hype Cycle for the Internet of Things, 2020 – *https://www.primekey.com/ gartner-report-hype-cycle-for-the-internet-of-things/*

Gartner – Hype Cycle for Digital Marketing & Hype Cycle for Digital Advertising, 2020 – *https://www.smartinsights.com/managing-digital-marketing/marketing-innovation/ technology-for-innovation-in-marketing/*

IEEE – Computer Society 2022 Report – *https://www.computer.org/publications/ tech-news/trends/2022-report*

INFO-TECH – 2021 Tech Trends – *https://www.infotech.com/sem/lp4/2021-tech-trends*

Intent – 8 IoT trends to watch in 2020 and beyond – *https://withintent.com/ blog/8-iot-trends-to-watch-in-2020-&-beyond/*

McKinsey – Artificial-intelligence hardware: New opportunities for semiconductor companies – *https://www.mckinsey.com/~/media/McKinsey/Industries/Semiconductors/*

Our%20Insights/Artificial%20intelligence%20hardware%20New%20opportunities%20 for%20semiconductor%20companies/Artificial-intelligence-hardware.ashx

McKinsey – The top trends in Tech – Executive summary – *https://www. mckinsey.com/~/media/mckinsey/Business%20Functions/McKinsey%20 Digital/Our%20Insights/The%20top%20trends%20in%20tech%20final/ Top-trends-in-tech-executive-summary-6-24-21*

MIT – 10 Breakthrough Technologies 2021 – *https://www.technologyreview. com/2021/02/24/1014369/10-breakthrough-technologies-2021/*

OECD – 21st Century Technologies: Promises and Perils of a Dynamic Future – *https:// www.oecd.org/futures/35391210.pdf*

Pluralsight – Tech in 2025: 10 Technologies that will Transform the Global Economy – *https://www.pluralsight.com/blog/career/tech-in-2025*

The Pourquoi Pas – Tech's "Next Big Thing": 20 Technologies that will change your life by 2050 – *https://www.thepourquoipas.com/post/the-next-big-thing-2050-technologies*

Science Focus – Future technology: 25 ideas about to change our world – *https://www.sciencefocus.com/future-technology/ future-technology-22-ideas-about-to-change-our-world/*

Framework 3: Navigating the Future—50 Critical Questions

By Rohit Talwar and Karolina Dolatowska

What critical questions should we asking ourselves at the global, organizational, and personal level to help map a path to the future?

The chapters of this book have highlighted countless possibilities, scenarios, choices, and questions shaping the future for individuals, societies, nations, governments, and organizations. In keeping with the diversity of perspectives in this book, we believe there is no single set of imperatives, no single set of decisions, and no single five-step plan that will work for every reader and organization. We believe that there are eight billion plus different paths that will be taken to the future by the individuals, communities, societies, nations, governments, and organizations that inhabit the planet today.

Hence, in this concluding chapter, we have tried to help in the mapping of those paths by consolidating some of the many ideas and possibilities into 50 questions across seven domains covering the operating environment, economy, individuals and civil society, critical sectors, business and investment, politics and government, and science and technology. We hope they stimulate wide-range thinking for vibrant dialog for our readers and the different community ecosystems they are part of, from families and spiritual networks through to organizations and nations. We make no apologies for the provocations, dinner table disputes, and boardroom busts-ups that could ensue!!!

Operating Environment

1. *Priorities*—How can we adapt our views, change our behaviors, and collaborate globally to ensure that we put climate change, planetary protection, and human wellbeing at the top of our priority list?
2. *Change*—What are the critical changes we might see across political, economic, social, environmental, and technological domains in the next 12 months and 12 years?
3. *Choices*—Which of the changes we are experiencing, and the decisions we are making, today could be most significant in shaping future mindsets, shifts, impacts, risks, opportunities, and scenarios?
4. *Culture*—What kind of culture could emerge as the world adapts to the possibility of social distancing, mask wearing, and regular vaccination becoming a regular or permanent feature in society, and how might this impact relationships between individuals within a nation, and between nations?
5. *Opportunities*—As this planetary crisis evolves, how best can we uncover and realise exciting opportunities as well as spotting new forms of global risk and danger?
6. *Sustainability*—What if the solution to our biggest global challenges was to combine ecology with technology in a human-centric and sustainable manner?

Economy

7. *Resilience*—What lessons have been learned from the different economic responses to the pandemic adopted around the world, and how can we use best practices to enhance the resilience of national and global economic systems?

8. *Rebuilding*—What are the most critical economic strategies and measures required nationally and globally to recover and drive an inclusive and sustainable economic recovery?

9. *Volatility*—How can we transform financial systems and markets to eliminate some of the volatility that can destabilize economies at the national, regional, and global level?

10. *Crypto Economy*—How might the applications of block-chain-based crypto assets and decentralized finance solutions disrupt fiat currencies, transform traditional financial services markets, and lay the foundations for a new crypto-based global economy?

11. *Governance*—How might artificial intelligence (AI) be leveraged to ensure more efficient, stable, transparent, and sustainable operation of economies and financial markets?

12. *Currencies*—When might we shift to a single global currency and what impact could that have on the economies and sovereignty of individual nations?

13. *Alternatives*—What are the most promising new economic philosophies and models that could ensure a more stable and economic future for all of humanity?

14. *Debt*—Can we envisage a world without debt and what impacts could that have on individuals, businesses, and nations?

Individuals and Civil Society

15. *Destiny*—How can we help individuals take control of their own futures, ensuring that their learning, capabilities, assumptions, and mindsets are being updated and evolving constantly to keep pace with a changing world?

16. *Sovereignty*—In a world of deeper penetration of digital into our lives, closer surveillance and scrutiny of our activities, and gradual erosion of our privacy, how can we maintain control of our identities and make choices over how much of an "off grid" lifestyle we want to pursue?

17. *Equity and Inequality*—Is it desirable to have a fairer distribution of assets, wealth, rewards, and access to opportunity across all societal domains, and how might we bring that about?

18. *Inclusivity*—How can we expand our bounds of possibility and openness to embrace the diversity of races, cultures, histories, gender choices, identity preferences, relationship models, household structures, philosophical and political outlooks, and multidimensional differences of which global society is comprised today?

19. *Mindsets*—How might social and psychological factors shape the new normal of post-pandemic society?

20. *Generations*—How might millennials, Gen Z, and other generations respond to the post-pandemic period?

21. *Wellbeing*—Looking back at the pandemic from 2025, what legacy might we have left regarding our attitude toward physical activity and wellbeing, and how might it be impacted by technology?

22. *Finances*—How might the pandemic impact our personal financial strategies and choices in planning for retirement?

23. *Globality*—How can we establish common approaches to global protection of human rights, ethics, and standards of behavior, and is this desirable?

Critical Sectors

24. *Healthcare*—How can we best balance the need for robust public health with the desire for personal freedom, privacy, and equality of opportunity?

25. *Health Systems*—Over the next few years, how might the pandemic era public health monitoring technologies, developed for governments and corporations, be used against us?

26. *Schooling*—How might schools and relationships with the community of parents, educators, and students change in a post-pandemic future?

27. *Public Education*—How might the post-pandemic economic recovery and possible shifts in the political landscape shape the future of public education?

28. *Higher Education*—What are the most surprising or unexpected plausible future scenarios imaginable for the return to university beyond the pandemic?

29. *Food*—What does this global pandemic reveal to us about the opportunities and vulnerabilities of our global food system, supply chains, and food security that could be addressed through key technological advances?

30. *Mobility*—What regulatory, economic, and behavioral changes might be required to create an efficient, green, and economically viable clean global mobility ecosystem in the wake of the pandemic?

Business and Investment

31. *Outlook*—Could the pandemic be the catalyst for businesses to embrace bigger picture thinking and smarter localized decision-making?

32. *Recovery*—How can the most pandemic ravaged sectors—such as travel, aviation, hospitality, leisure, and entertainment—transform and future-proof themselves in an environment of constant turbulence?

33. *Disruption*—How could the pandemic impact traditional sectors that are already being disrupted by digital technologies, SectorTech, new entrants, and an increasingly changing role in the marketplace?

34. *Investment*—How can we ensure a sufficient focus is placed on longer-term research and development in critical social, environmental, scientific, and technological fields alongside opportunities that are closer to markets?

35. *Rewards*—Which investment models might allow for greater citizen participation in the funding of more speculative

developments and ensure that the returns on investment are shared more equitably between private investors and wider society?

36. *Focus*—How can we reframe organizational thinking away from change management toward change readiness to help prepare us for an uncertain future?

37. *Capability*—What are the critical leadership and managerial skills required to help organizations navigate a path to the future?

Politics and Government

38. *Geopolitics*—How might the 2020 pandemic accelerate and influence future geopolitical developments?

39. *Relationships*—How might the economic and political fallout from the pandemic impact international relations and society over the next five years?

40. *Security*—How might the pandemic experience shape national security planning in the new normal?

41. *Continents*—What scenarios could emerge for the future of each continent in a post-pandemic world?

42. *Transformation*—How can the government and companies of the most affected countries "hear the future" and take action to be successful in the post-pandemic era?

43. *Responsibility*—How can the public sector in urban and rural communities respond to the enormous challenges of serving their diverse populations with civic and social services while also dealing with the negative forces of global pandemics?

Science and Technology

44. *Readiness*—What can we do to raise the understanding of emerging science and technology developments and accelerate the acquisition of deep digital literacy across society?

45. *Ethics*—Is it possible or desirable to create globally accepted ethical standards and codes of conduct across all fields of science

and technology? If so, how can we make this happen and enforce their application?

46. *Digitization*—How might digital ecosystems evolve to help accelerate post-pandemic recovery, and what do leaders need to understand to assess the possible industry impacts?

47. *Timelines*—What are the technology evolution timelines we should have on our radar as we map out strategies for the next 5-10 years and beyond?

48. *Transhumanism*—What might the implications for society be of pursuing scientific advances that offer the promise of augmenting human capabilities and radically extending life expectancy?

49. *Automation*—How can we prepare for and adapt to the growth of entirely digital decentralized autonomous organizations (DAOs) with no employees, enabled by advances in artificial intelligence, work automation, and blockchain smart contracts?

50. *Meltdown*—How might individuals, societies, governments, and organizations respond and adapt to a catastrophic failure and shutdown of the global technology and communications infrastructure that underpins so much of human activity, whether through natural shocks (e.g. solar flares), or malicious actions?

Rohit Talwar is a global futurist and the CEO of Fast Future with a particular focus on the impact of emerging technologies on individuals, society, businesses, and governments.

Karolina Dolatowska is a foresight researcher and the business manager at Fast Future.

References

1 UN Sustainable Development Goals *https://sdgs.un.org/goals*

2 Intergovernmental Panel on Climate Change (IPCC) Sixth Assessment Report, Climate Change 2021: The Physical Science Basis *https://www.ipcc.ch/assessment-report/ar6*

3 How Much Would it Cost to End Climate Change?, Global Giving, March 1st, 2021, *https://www.globalgiving.org/learn/cost-to-end-climate-change*

4 University of Helsinki / Reaktor Elements of AI Course, *https://www.elementsofai.com*

5 Global Infrastructure Hub Outlook, *https://outlook.gihub.org*

6 A \$2 Trillion Plan to Bring Two Billion More People into the Digital Age, Boston Consulting Group, September 2020, *https://www.bcg.com/en-gb/publications/2020/plan-to-bring-high-speed-internet-access-to-two-billion-people*

7 *https://www.oxfam.org.uk/media/press-releases/worlds-22-richest-men-have-more-wealth-than-all-the-women-in-africa*

8 *https://www.oxfam.org/en/press-releases/worlds-billionaires-have-more-wealth-46-billion-people*

9 *https://triple-a.io/crypto-ownership*

10 *https://www.bbc.co.uk/news/technology-55486157*

11 *https://www.forbes.com/sites/jonyounger/2020/04/22/your-leaders-need-help-adapting-to-our-new-world-of-work-meet-aceup/?sh=572a0d9229ca*

12 *https://www.transamericacenter.org/docs/default-source/retirement-survey-of-workers/tcrs2019_sr_19th-annual_worker_compendium.pdf*

13 Ben Steverman, Half of Older Americans Have Nothing in Retirement Savings, Forbes, 26 March 2019 *https://www.bloomberg.com/news/articles/2019-03-26/ almost-half-of-older-americans-have-zero-in-retirement-savings*

14 *https://www.cnbc.com/2020/04/09/ray-dalio-predicts-coronavirus-depression-this-is-bigger-than-2008.html*

15 *https://www.nytimes.com/2020/04/02/health/stem-cell-treatment-coronavirus.html*

16 *https://www.scmp.com/economy/china-economy/article/3093218/ belt-and-road-initiative-debt-how-big-it-and-whats-next*

17 Jerome C Glenn and Theodore J Gordon (Eds). 2009. Futures Research Methodology—V3.0. Millennium Project, chapter 6. *http://www.millennium-project.org/ publications-2/#method*

18 Arnold J Toynbee. 1946. A Study of History. New York: Oxford University Press, p. 273.

19 Spanish, meaning "There is no tomorrow," describing the local culture of living for today and not caring about the future.

20 Deloitte, 2019 *https://www2.deloitte.com/insights/us/en/focus/digital-maturity/ digital-innovation-ecosystems-organizational-agility.html*

21 Accenture, 2018 *https://insuranceblog.accenture.com/ how-susceptible-are-insurers-to-disruption-really*

22 Insurance Journal, 2020 *https://www.insurancejournal.com/news/ national/2019/11/07/547850.htm*

23 Insurance Thought Leadership, 2020 *https://www.insurancethoughtleadership.com/ InsurTech-a-decade-gone-a-decade-ahead*

24 Accenture, 2018 *https://newsroom.accenture.com/news/insurers-that-transform-their-businesses-and-operating-models-could-see-us-375-billion-in-new-revenue-growth-accenture-analysis-finds.htm*

25 Raconteur, 2020 *https://res.cloudinary.com/yumyoshojin/image/upload/v1/pdf/ future-insurance-2020.pdf*

26 Juniper Research, 2020 *https://www.juniperresearch.com/press/press-releases/ global-ai-insurance-premiums-exceed-20-bn-2024*

27 CapGemini/World InsurTech Report, 2020 *https://worldInsurTechreport.com/ resources/transforming-into-inventive-insurer-for-marketplace-successs*

28   As of June 2021, through the Department of Education, NYC public schools served 1.13 million students in over 1,800 schools. *https://www.schools.nyc.gov/about-us/ reports/doe-data-at-a-glance*

29   After the school shutdown was announced, the Department of Education set up 400 feeding hubs where anyone could pick up multiple free meals. *https://www.schools.nyc. gov/school-life/food/free-meals*

30   Millennium Project *http://www.millennium-project.org*

31   UN Sustainable Development Goals *https://sdgs.un.org/goals*

32   The Nine Planetary Boundaries, Stockholm Resilience Centre, *https://www. stockholmresilience.org/research/planetary-boundaries/the-nine-planetary-boundaries. html*

FAST FUTURE SERVICES AND PUBLICATIONS

Fast Future's services and publications are designed to help businesses, governments, NGOs, communities, and individuals to anticipate and navigate the emerging future, with a focus on widening perspectives, deepening insight, and enabling action. Our services can be customized to each client's unique priorities, requirements, and context. Our books are aimed at leaders, change agents, foresight practitioners, and anyone with an interest in the future.

Keynote Speaking—Fast Future and our contributors offer highly tailored live and virtual presentations using a range of formats and interactive approaches. Topics covered include driving forces shaping the emerging future; short, medium, and longer term scenarios; explorations of industry specific trends, innovations, and future possibilities; deep dives on digital transformation and exponentially advancing technologies such as artificial intelligence; introductions to the concepts and potential applications of emerging developments such as the crypto economy; and motivational talks on foresight driven organizations and leading from the future.

Consultancy—Our consultancy focuses on helping organizations undertake foresight and scenario building exercises and use the insights to spot market shifts, identify opportunities and risks, and surface challenges to current assumptions and plans. These are used to help adapt strategies, business models, innovation programs, and critical projects.

Bespoke Research and Scenario Planning—We conduct tailored horizon scans, scenarios, and deep dive studies for clients to use as thought leadership with their customers and for use within organizations.

Executive Foresight Mentorship and Coaching—One-to-one and small group work to help leaders develop foresight capabilities and apply them in different organizational contexts. Such applications typically range from strategy development and business prioritization through to opportunity identification and operational planning.

Foresight Training—Highly tailored programs designed to introduce key foresight concepts, approaches, frameworks, tools, and resources. The content and session structure are designed to help participants apply foresight for a range of organizational needs and address practical implementation questions and challenges that arise when introducing such approaches. These programs help create a common organizational language and framework that can accelerate the adoption and impact of foresight on decision-making.

Crypto Economy Programs—Customized courses designed to help organizations accelerate their understanding of crypto assets (currencies and tokens), the applications they enable, and the blockchain platforms that support them. A wide range of examples are used to help deepen participant understanding, demonstrate how other businesses are approaching crypto, and identify potential crypto strategies and opportunities for their own organizations.

Books—These are designed to provide stimulating, thought provoking, and action inspiring insights. Using a succinct and readable chapter format, each book explores key aspects of the factors shaping the future, how they might interact and play out, and the resulting risks, opportunities, and choices they create for us today.

Fast Future Books
and Reports

The following books and reports are all available for purchase or free download from our bookstore at www.fastfuture.com

FUTURE IN FOCUS—The Future of the Crypto Economy (Free Download)

This report draws on in-depth research and a global survey of active participants in the crypto economy and those new to it. The study explores individual and corporate views on key topics. At the individual level, these include the type and duration of involvement in crypto assets, investment drivers, expectations of sector performance over different time frames, barriers to individual adoption, current and future crypto asset invement preferences, assessment of the likely best performing categories of crypto assets, preferred investment routes, views on the evoloution of crypto, and likely ranking of asset class performance over the one year and four to 10 year+ time frames.

The study also looks at the corporate and governmental approach to crypto assets and discusses key financial applications, crypto investment strategies, current and future levels of crypto holdings on balanace sheets, barriers to business adoption, key operational applications of blockchain technology, views on Central Bank Digital Currencies (CBDCs), responses to and engagement with countries adoping crypto assets as legal tender, and organizational views on the evoloution of the crypto economy.

AFTERSHOCKS AND OPPORTUNITIES–Scenarios for a Post-Pandemic Future

What different scenarios, challenges, and possibilities are emerging for our post-pandemc future?

An Opportunity for Fresh Perspectives

While the world grapples with the current unfolding crisis, as futurists we know how important it is to also be thinking about the next horizon and beyond. This can help ensure that the decisions we make today do not simply lay the foundation for a new set of problems over the horizon. Equally, understanding the types of future that might emerge post-crisis can help us plan and prepare for those possibilities as we reshape our strategies today. Finally, such future insights might help us spot, train for, and adapt to the new opportunities, risks, and challenges that could arise as a post-pandemic world unfolds.

A Global Collaboration

In response to the need for future perspectives, Fast Future wanted to create this fast track book, which draws on the expertise, insight, ambition, and vision of 25 future thinkers from around the world. The goal is to provide individuals, leaders, and organizations with foresight, insight, challenge, visionary thinking, and navigational guidance on what lies ahead.

Scenarios for A Post-Pandemic Future

The common goal of this group of writers is to provide provocations that will take the public discourse beyond the current debate. The aim is to acknowledge the importance of critical future shaping forces, developments, and ideas, and think about how we can create a safer and more sustainable world beyond infection and mortality rates, testing strategies, personal protective equipment, lockdown policies, vaccination, and economic support. As many have said, a crisis is an ideal time to reset our thinking, refocus our strategies and policies, and try new ideas designed to lay the foundation for the next future and what comes after that. A future that the authors believe can be fairer, more inclusive, more transparent, and more sustainable for all.

Four Core Themes

The concise, insightful, and action enabling ideas and provocations in this book are presented as an exploration of possible scenarios and development paths across four key domains that we believe should be of interest to politicians, business leaders, civil society activitists, and most importantly, the ordinary citizens of this planet:

1. *Critical Shifts*—exploring the developments taking place across every aspect of our collective thinking as a result of the pandemic experience.

2. *Society and Social Policy*—examining the implications and opportunities for the fabric and infrastructure of society as we look to tackle both the existing persistent challenges and the new ones that have arisen through the crisis, framing an agenda for what could be developed in what many commentators are calling the future "new normal."

3. *Government and Economy*—assessing how governments are, and should be, grappling with the challenges and consequences of balancing health protection with economic recovery during and post-pandemic.

4. *Business and Technology*—outlining the possible implications, opportunities, and choices for business and our use of technology. Exploring how we might solve critical questions posed by the pandemic and lay the foundation for the future across health, education, social structures, commerce, and the design of our organizations.

OPPORTUNITY AT THE EDGE–Change, Challenge, and Transformation on the Path to 2025 (Free Download)

Opportunity at the Edge was developed by Fast Future on behalf of and in collaboration with Aruba. Edge technologies are designed to shift power from the center to the edge of computing ecosystems and thus enable the processing and analysis of user data at the point where people connect to a network. The study explores how such developments could revolutionize corporate strategies; create more dynamic, responsive, and personalized customer and employee experiences; enable powerful business and revenue models; and even catalyze the growth of entirely new industries. To unlock these opportunities, the book argues that enterprises must embrace fundamental change, engaging in widespread strategic, structural, and leadership transformation.

Morten Illum, VP EMEA at Aruba, comments: "The findings in this book highlight the vast commercial potential for enterprises utilizing edge technologies, if companies are willing and able to enact the considerable organizational changes needed. The edge represents a dramatic overhaul in how companies understand, service, and meet the needs of their customers and employees. It will be a world defined by dynamic, immediate, and personalized services."

A VERY HUMAN FUTURE–Enriching Humanity in a Digitized World

As society enters the fourth industrial revolution, a major question arises—can we harness intense technological bursts of possibility to bring about a better world? *A Very Human Future* illustrates how the evolution of society, cities, people, businesses, industries, nations, and governments are becoming entangled in unexpected ways by exponential technological disruption. This is not a book about technology but an exploration of how we make it serve humanity's highest needs and ambitions. Each chapter looks at how new ideas enabled by emerging technologies are straining the old social fabric, and proposes radical future scenarios, strategies, and actions to safeguard humanity from harm and enhance opportunity for all. This book is a manifesto for a future that is better than the past.

A Very Human Future rejects an outlook where human beings live a mundane existence while technologies burst with possibility. Rather, we use this book to endorse a proactive approach to the future where technology is designed to benefit humanity purposefully and intentionally. To advocate for a very human future we ask, for example, how do we use technology to overcome gender bias or to impart a meaningful education to new generations? Can artificial intelligence tools make government more trustworthy and help us deal with the impacts of automation replacing humans? What rights should people have when residing in smart cities? The scale of the new technologies requires a protective logic for moving forward, keeping humanity at the center so that we avoid dehumanizing ourselves and future generations.

A Very Human Future is not one, but many positive stories and visions of the future that can be powerful beacons for social adaptation. We argue that the time to shape the narrative of the future and stake a claim for humanity is now. *A Very Human Future* uses knowledge as power, describing surprising ways that new thinking and disruptive technology can impact society. This book explains that protecting what's human is the key to retaining our dominance over future technological progress.

BEYOND GENUINE STUPIDITY–Ensuring AI Serves Humanity

This book explores critical emerging issues arising from the rapid pace of development in artificial intelligence (AI). The authors argue for a forward-looking and conscious approach to AI development and deployment to ensure that it genuinely serves humanity's best interests. Through a series of articles, they present a compelling case to get beyond the genuine stupidity of narrow, short-term, and alarmist thinking and look at AI from a long-term holistic perspective. The reality is that AI will impact current sectors and jobs—and hopefully enable new ones.

A smart approach requires us to think about and experiment with strategies for adopting and absorbing the impacts of AI—encompassing education systems, reskilling the workforce, unemployment, guaranteed basic incomes, robot taxes, job creation, encouraging new ventures, research and development to enable tomorrow's industries, and dealing with the mental health impacts. The book explores the potential implications for sectors ranging from healthcare and automotive, to legal and education. The challenges for business itself are also examined from leadership and HR, to sales and business ethics.

THE FUTURE REINVENTED–Reimagining Life, Society, and Business

This book explores the future transformations that could arise from the disruptive technological, scientific, social, and economic developments shaping the decade ahead. The authors offer a range of unique visions of different aspects of a future in which the very tenets of reality are undergoing deep and vital transformations. Through a series of chapters organized into three sections (transformations in life, industries, and business), they present holistic future scenarios that encourage strategic thinking about what lies beyond the hype.

Using a long-term futurist perspective, *The Future Reinvented* offers glimpses of the future in different business sectors and functions such as legal, automotive, and sales, as well as in different areas of everyday life like retirement, education, and health. Audiences will appreciate the vivid imagery which brings to life a number of different "futures," including workplace scenarios where people work side by side with artificial intelligence or robotic colleagues, can obtain physical enhancements to become smarter, stronger, or more psychologically resilient, or reside in a post-jobs world. The book provides a solid foundation for scenario thinking and planning, identifying signals of change, and interpreting signposts that serve as early warning signs of emerging futures.

THE FUTURE OF BUSINESS–Critical insights to a rapidly changing world from 62 future thinkers

The Future of Business is aimed at the leaders of today and the pioneers of tomorrow. Our intention is to provide a broad perspective on the key forces, trends, developments, and ideas that could redefine our world over the next two decades. The goal is to highlight how these future factors are shaping the opportunities, challenges, implications, and resulting choices for those driving the future of business. The book draws on the ideas of 62 futurists, future thinkers, and experts in a range of domains from 22 countries on four continents. *The Future of Business* highlights how—in a world of constant and ever-more fundamental change—those charged with leadership, management, and stewardship of large and small organizations alike are faced with a set of questions many of us never thought we would have to confront.

This book is designed to provide wide-ranging visions of future possibilities and take us on a tour of the forces shaping the political, economic, and social environment. We explore the advances in science and technology that could have the greatest impact on society and drive business disruption. We examine the implications of these for how business will need to evolve and the new industries that could emerge over the next two decades. We highlight key tools, approaches, and ways of thinking about the future that can help organizations embed foresight at the heart of the management model. We conclude with a framework that highlights key choices we face in shaping the Future of Business.

The Air Transport 2035 Reports (Free Download)

Working in partnership with Future Travel Experience, we have developed these free reports exploring key aspects of the near- and long-term future of the Air Transport Sector in the post-pandemic era. The reports are:

COVID-19 Air Transport Near-Term Impacts and Scenarios

This report shares the findings of an industry survey, expert interviews, desk research, and analysis to explore the impacts of the pandemic on the sector and presents scenarios for its possible near-term evolution. The detailed results cover the immediate and full year impact on flights, passenger numbers, and revenues; expectations for the timing of peak impact; recovery timescales; redundancies; people and skills development priorities; finance and operations strategies; longer-term operating assumptions and tactics; future financial and ownership assumptions and tactics; investment priorities; procurement implications; critical response priorities, strategies, and tactics; implications for longer-term sector strategy; and key learnings from the sector's response to the pandemic to date.

The Impacts of COVID-19 on Innovation and Digital Transformation in Air Transport

This report highlights the results of an industry survey, expert interviews, desk research, and analysis to explore how the pandemic is shaping approaches to innovation and digital transformation across the sector. The detailed results cover the response to COVID-19 in terms of changes to the terminal environment, technology use in the airport environment, impact on cabin configuration and in-flight experience, longer-term airport and airline innovation priorities and developments, impact on digital transformation and collaboration strategies, and implications for innovation and digital transformation budgets and longer-term strategies.

Available soon from Fast Future

50:50—Scenarios for the Next 50 Years

This book explores scenarios for the next 50 years, with 50 perspectives on possible futures across a range of topic areas, written by 50 different future thinkers from around the world. The book is designed to have the broadest possible scope and is edited by global futurists Rohit Talwar, Steve Wells, and Alexandra Whittington.

Future Publications

The landscape for potential publication topics is evolving rapidly and we are excited at the prospects of working on multi-author books or partnering with innovative organizations who share our passion for exploring the future. We are currently considering books on a range of future related themes.

We are always interested to hear from organizations who want to develop future focused thought leadership content for their clients, and individual future thinkers who want to bring their ideas, knowledge, and insights to market with Fast Future.

Visit www.fastfuture.com for more information.

AFTERSHOCKS AND OPPORTUNITIES— SCENARIOS FOR A POST-PANDEMIC FUTURE

The Change Agenda for a Post-Pandemic World

By Rohit Talwar, Steve Wells, and Alexandra Whittington

What are the critical fragilities and opportunities that have to be part of the agenda recovery and future development at national and global level?

As the authors have demonstrated so vividly across the chapters of this book, there are many critical aspects to building a post-pandemic world; one that is fair, open, inclusive, sustainable, and rich in opportunities for all. The current crisis has surfaced a number of fragilities at the individual, societal, national, and international level. These have either been well understood but patchily addressed in the past, or are issues to which some or all are genuinely blindsided.

Fragilities also present the opportunity for genuinely new thinking and innovation. So, we conclude the book with what we consider to be ten key agenda items that we and the individual authors in this book believe will have to be part of the recovery agenda at national and global level.

1. Individual Financial Security and Sustainability

The crisis has highlighted that some people literally do not have enough savings to see them through the next month, week, or day. While for many, there was a vague acknowledgment of this as we went about our daily lives, it didn't truly seep into our consciousness or influence our behavior. Now, the massive expansion of people using foodbanks, coupled with the sight of mass population feeding programs in developing countries, has highlighted the scale of the problem and how far we have to go to resolve it—if that is seen as a priority.

Making real impact on the first two UN Sustainable Development Goals (SDGs) of "No Poverty" and "Zero Hunger" implies achieving a level of long-term individual sustainability. Governments will come under intense pressure to rethink social policy and to assess the suitability of welfare payments against broader questions of how long an individual or family can last with the money on offer. As a result, the debate about the need for some form of universal basic income (UBI) and services will inevitably rise in volume and intensity.

2. Health and Elder Care Systems and Access

The crisis has highlighted multiple issues around the level of provision, health and care worker salaries, resourcing levels, personal protective equipment (PPE), testing, logistics and distribution, managerial preparedness, resilience, and emergency planning. Every system globally will need to rethink its strategies, funding models, structures, early warning systems, and crisis protocols for a world where the awareness of the range of impending health risks has been heightened.

The poor state of people's finances has also left many with little or no ability to pay for care and limited access to emergency public provision. The funding of, and access to, healthcare for all could become an issue on which governments rise and fall.

3. Mental Health and Physical Safety

The number of cases of stress and other mental health conditions has seen a continuous rise in the last few years. The cost to society across multiple dimensions from healthcare to business interruption had already been estimated in the trillions of dollars. Now, during the pandemic, the loss of jobs, businesses, and freedoms amongst the old and young alike are reported to be driving up the volume and severity of stress and other mental health issues across society. For governments, there will be issues around the extent to which they want to intervene, ensuring access, the capacity to serve growing demand, and the funding of such services.

A related issue is that globally, there has been a clear, and in some cases massive, rise in reported cases of domestic abuse, calls to help-lines, and the unseen suffering of those not in a position to ask for help. Once the recovery starts, non-interventionist governments in particular are going to be challenged to determine the priority placed on such matters. The resulting choices will have far-reaching implications for funding of support services from social services and policing through to healthcare and education.

4. National Preparedness

The crisis has put a spotlight on the huge differences in the level of preparedness and capacity for rapid action in different nations around the world. Some had well tested procedures to mobilize travel restrictions, and enact mass testing, tracing, and quarantine measures. They also had systems and policy options in place to be able to carry out a diverse range of support measures. These range from calling up reservist health workers and making direct payments to the population, through to mobilizing volunteers and communities at scale. Others seemed, and still appear to be, incapable or leaden footed in their actions. This will raise the debate about the need for national mechanisms for horizon scanning and foresight, risk assessment, anticipatory contingency and disaster planning, and resilient resourcing to enable rapid scale-up in emergencies.

5. Funding

Most nations have looked to debt, quantitative easing, and the printing of money to fund their way through the emergency medical and economic response programs they have had to implement. The question is how, or if, these bills will be paid. The general trend over the last two decades or more has been to drive down taxes in the hope that greater wealth in the economy will raise everyone's living standards. The crisis has highlighted that this isn't really working anywhere near as well as policy makers might have hoped in many countries across the globe.

The crisis has been expensive, the cost of recovery is as yet unknown as we face the prospect of prolonged national recessions or even a global depression. Nations may be forced to reverse taxation policy as they look to corporations, higher earners, and the wealthy to provide more of the funding to restart economies currently stuck in reverse gear. The alternative could be massive cuts in public services and government spending, resulting in prolonged periods of austerity—with all the social consequences such measures bring.

The specter of mass technological unemployment was already on the horizon due to the rise of automation technologies and artificial intelligence (AI) in particular. This in turn had driven the debate over the potential for introducing a UBI—and how it might be funded— with options ranging from taxes on wealth, financial transactions, or the deployment of AI and robotics. These mechanisms are now back in the spotlight as countries wrestle with how to pay the bill for the pandemic and finance the economic and social recovery.

6. Government and Governance

The challenge for every government is to find the right future governance, engagement, and representation models for populations that have probably never placed the actions of their political leaders under such close examination. National governments have come under intense scrutiny during the pandemic. The spotlight has been placed on their level of foresight, disaster preparedness, and capacity to make crucial decisions in the middle of a crisis. Equally questions are being asked about how well the lessons are being learned both for the next stage of the crisis and for the future. Issues of transparency, honesty, planning assumptions, and priorities are all coming to the fore as populations ask whether their governments are doing a good job.

At the same time, governments are using a variety of community mechanisms and technology tools to innovate solutions to the myriad of issues and needs that arise. Decisions about the use of emergency powers and citizen surveillance tracking and tracing tools are raising questions about the future protection of civil liberties and privacy. Stay at home orders have driven many civil servants to work from home. Hence, questions are also being raised about how effectively the work of governments can be delivered from our dining tables while home schooling our children.

7. Global Institutions

The World Health Organization has come under severe criticism from some quarters and been seen by others as an essential resource and partner in navigating the crisis. The United Nations and global financial institutions such as the World Bank have been visible, but the question is how impactful they have been. The remit and rules of engagement for these institutions are set by their member and donor states. The key questions now are whether those rules are the right ones and whether these global organizations are truly fit for purpose when it comes to global crisis where coordinated solutions are required. If the answer is at least a partial no, then how do we go about modernizing or replacing them, who will fund them, and how can we ensure greater effectiveness than the existing entities they are replacing?

8. Weak and Failing Nations

There is growing concern that the crisis will cause chaos in nations already on the brink of collapse such as Afghanistan, Syria, and Yemen. Some estimates suggest that these and other under-resourced and overstretched nations could see three million or more deaths from the pandemic. The question is how such nations can map a path to the future. Do they effectively seek protection from other states, merge into larger entities, or become the testbed for radical new models of post-conflict, post-crisis government and governance?

9. Coordination of Global Power

Many would argue that in the Global Financial Crisis of 2007-2008, the worst-case scenario of total economic collapse was avoided through the coordinated efforts of the wealthiest nations in the G7 and G20 groupings. However, this time round, they have been noticeable by their absence and their inability to even issue joint communiques over how they are coming together to tackle what is a truly global problem. Without the wealth, resources, and mobilization capabilities of these nations acting together, the crisis could stretch out far longer than the 12- to 24-month window that many are predicting.

10. The Business of Business and the Environment

The crisis has raised a number of interesting questions over the future role and purpose of business and how we truly balance the quadruple bottom line of people, planet, purpose, and prosperity. The UN Sustainable Development Goals (SDGs) have become an increasingly important filter through which businesses run their strategies, and that focus is likely to increase. Some argue that this is the beginning of the end of capitalism in its current form and that new models need to be tested that result in a fairer distribution of wealth and resources.

The slowdown of economic activity has had a powerful impact on the environment with marked declines in emissions and air pollution. Natural habitats have blossomed, and rarely spotted animal species have become more visible. The planet has been given the chance to rest and recuperate from the frenetic pace of human activity. The issues now are whether those gains can be sustained as economic activity ramps up and what priority governments and businesses place on the environment as they seek to recover from the financial impacts of the pandemic.

The advent of exponential technologies such as AI and synthetic biology offer the potential for deep and dramatic transformation of every sector and the unleashing of economic abundance. The question arises as to how the spoils will be divided and what happens to those whose roles are replaced by the technology. If new jobs are to be created for these new sectors, then who will bear the cost of retraining the workforce?

Governments are providing and promising a wide range of financial support measures to help businesses through the crisis. There is a question over the extent to which these rescue packages are being tied to environmental, social, innovation, and job creation goals. Ultimately, the question will need to be asked as to what businesses think their role is in tomorrow's world and what responsibilities they bear to the environment and wider society?

The crisis is raising fundamental questions at every level and creating once in a lifetime challenges for those in power. Many are still wrestling with the complexities of containment and exit strategies and have little bandwidth for broader medium- to long-term considerations. Others are beginning to understand that the crisis represents both a turning point and a time for fundamental reflection. What are the goals for human life, society, nations, and the globe that we want to enable on the other side of the pandemic? Fortunately, we have the SDGs as a start point for that reflection—the question will be how big our appetite is to use this opportunity to drive fundamental changes in our destiny.

- *What should governments prioritize as they lay out the change agenda for the next one, five, and ten years?*
- *Do societal health, mental wellbeing, and physical security have to take a back seat as governments focus on restarting the economic engine?*
- *How can we ensure that delivering on the Sustainable Development Goals becomes even more central to the delivery of national recovery plans and corporate strategies for the near to medium term?*

(Full version available at fastfuture.com)